STORIES FOR GROWING

STORIES FOR GROWING

ALICE GEER KELSEY

NEW YORK · NASHVILLE

ABINGDON PRESS

STORIES FOR GROWING

SET UP, PRINTED, AND BOUND BY THE
PARTHENON PRESS, AT NASHVILLE,
TENNESSEE, UNITED STATES OF AMERICA

ACKNOWLEDGMENTS

All of these stories have appeared in periodicals. Acknowledgment and thanks are here expressed to the publishers, who have graciously permitted reprinting or adaptation in this collection.

To the American National Red Cross for "Ciro's Bigger World" from the American Junior Red Cross *News*.

To the Brethren Publishing House for "The Song of the Well," "A Farmer's Song," and "A Song of God's Steadfast Love" from *Journeys for Boys and Girls*.

To the Child Training Association for "Why Bats Fly at Night" and "Bartholdi's Mother" from *Children's Activities*.

To The Methodist Publishing House for "The Lost Song," "A Tall Tale Grows Short," and "The Battle of the Birthdays" from *Trails for Juniors*.

To Pan Pacific Centers, Inc., for "The Package from the Country" from *Asia Calling*.

To the Pilgrim Press for "A Lunch That Grew" and "Fair Are the Meadows" from *Children's Religion*.

To the Pulpit Digest Publishing Company for "The King's Horns," "The Hen, the Mouse, and the Rabbit," "The Cow That Counted Seven," "A Song of Worship," "A Song of Giving," "Songs of a New King," "The Battle That Never Was Fought," "The First New England Sabbath," "Slingshots and Church Bells," "The House That Prayer Built," "The Shepherd and the Wallet," "A Question from the FBI," "Don't Be a Mackerel," "Anita's Homework," "The Halfway Samaritan," "Thirty-Two Languages," "Noel, the Christmas Baby," and "The Mitten Tree" from *Pulpit Digest*.

5

CONTENTS

OLD, OLD TALES RETOLD

SONGS FROM THE OLD TESTAMENT

ACROSS THE CENTURIES

BOYS AND GIRLS TODAY

SEASONAL STORIES

OLD, OLD TALES RETOLD

WHY BATS FLY AT NIGHT

AN AFRICAN FOLK TALE

Long ago when the world Yataa created was new and fresh, there was little difference between day and night. The sun took care of the world by day and kept it hot and flooded with bright sunshine. The moon watched over the world by night and kept it comfortably cool with a pleasant light which was easy on the eyes—like dawn or like twilight. There was plenty of light for the men to plant their corn, for the women to weave their baskets, or for the children to model dolls and animals of clay.

One night when the moon was shedding its cool and pleasant light, Yataa called the Bat to him and said, "See this big covered basket. It is full of something called Darkness, something that has never been known in the world. I want you to carry it to the moon. Guard it every minute of your journey."

"What shall I do with it when I reach the moon?" asked the Bat. He could not refuse to do whatever Yataa asked, but he did wish to have complete directions. After all, it might be a longer journey to the moon than it looked to be. The Bat had never been there before.

"When you and the basket reach the moon," answered Yataa, "I will tell you what to do."

So the Bat tested the cover to see that it was carefully tied over this mysterious new thing, Darkness. Then he obediently lifted the basket onto his shoulder. He fixed his eye on the highest mountain peak, a good spot from which to take off into the blue. As he flew off, he heard the voice of Yataa repeating, "Guard Darkness carefully. Let none of it escape."

11

"I will guard it well," promised Bat.

The basket was heavy. By the time the Bat reached the tip of the mountain, he was ready for a rest. He set the basket down on the highest peak. Forgetting his promise to Yataa, he went off in search of food and a shady place for a nap. Naturally, the animals that lived on the mountain were quick to notice something new. Bush Goat and Bush Pig sniffed at the basket while Bat slept comfortably, upside down in a treetop. Sniffing, Bush Goat and Bush Pig walked round and round the basket.

"It does not have the smell of Man!" bleated Bush Goat. "I am not afraid of it!"

"Perhaps there is food in it!" grunted Bush Pig. "Let's open it and have a feast!"

So while Bat slept, Bush Goat and Bush Pig tugged and gnawed at the fastenings till they had loosened the cover. They were so busy satisfying their curiosity that they did not hear the whir of the big wings of Bat swooping toward them.

"Do not touch that basket!" squeaked Bat. "It belongs to Yataa. I am carrying it to the moon."

But his warnings came too late. The cover of the hamper was already open.

Out flew Darkness in a great cloud that covered the mountain and rolled down over the plain. Bush Pig and Bush Goat ran as fast as they could, but Darkness seemed to swallow them up. It was unbelievable that so much could be squeezed together in one basket. Darkness covered the other mountains, the sea, and the forest. It rolled on up into the sky. The moon still shone, high up in the sky; but it could not conquer this new thing which had been freed from the basket. Everywhere there was nothing but Darkness—Darkness—Darkness.

For a minute Bat was too stunned to stir. Then he knew what he must do. He must make up for disobeying Yataa. If it took him the rest of his life, he must gather Darkness and put it back in the basket. Yataa must be obeyed.

So, as long as the moon cared for the earth, Bat swooped hither and thither gathering up bits of the flowing Darkness and pushing them into the basket. But before he could make even a dent in his task, the sun came up to take his turn at ruling the earth—and Darkness went into hiding. By that time Bat was so completely exhausted that he would have needed a rest anyway. He found a cave where he could rest with his head hanging down and his big skin wings clinging to the rocks. He wondered if he had lost his chance ever to gather Darkness back into the basket and carry it to the moon; but when the sun set, Darkness came rushing back. Bat began again to catch Darkness and stuff it into the basket.

And to this day that has been the job of Bat, his children, and his grandchildren, down to more great-greats than you could possibly count. Every night bats can be seen swooping and darting over the earth, low over the ground or low over the water. They never give up hope of gathering Darkness into its hamper and carrying it to the moon. They are still working to make up for the careless disobedience of their great-grandfather Bat so many years ago.

Based on a paragraph in the chapter "The Idea of God Among the Kono of Sierra Leone" by Robert T. Parsons in *African Ideas of God*, edited by Edwin W. Smith (Edinburgh House Press, 1950).

THE KING'S HORNS

A PERSIAN FOLK TALE

Once upon a time in a country of the East there lived a king who was in great trouble. To be sure, he had a big palace, armies of soldiers, trains of camels, flocks of sheep, herds of goats, and chests full of treasure. But none of this wealth was of help to him in his distress.

On the king's forehead there appeared two small lumps, just in the edge of his hair. These lumps swelled and grew hard. Then the skin over them cracked. Out grew two horns, small at first but growing longer and harder with every day that passed. Ashamed to let anyone know what had happened, the king wore his turban low on his forehead to cover the disgraceful horns. Soon they were so long that they humped his turban. He changed to bigger and bigger turbans, which he wore night and day.

As the horns grew, the king's hair and beard grew also. Finally he could stand his uncomfortably long hair and his untidy beard no longer. He called a barber to his most private room and unwound his huge turban so that the man could trim his hair and shave him. The barber politely pretended not to notice.

When the barber's work was finished, the king could not trust him to go out into the world and keep the secret of the horns. He had the poor man put to death. This was repeated with a new barber every time the king needed a haircut and a shave.

Finally a barber named Akbar was called. He did his work and then was told that he could not go out alive.

"I will not tell anyone your secret, O King," pleaded the poor barber. "I'll not breathe a word about your horns, not even to my wife."

"I cannot trust you," said the king.

"But think how convenient it would be to have a regular barber." Akbar could think quickly when his life was in danger. "I would come to you whenever you needed me. You would not have to teach a new man your ways each time."

The king stroked his neatly trimmed beard and thought how handy it would be to have a barber who knew how he wanted the work done.

Akbar added a new argument. "You must know that there are not many barbers left in your kingdom. Soon you will have to send to faraway lands for them. They will neither speak nor understand your language."

"That would be inconvenient," mused the king. "Do you promise not to tell my secret to a living person?"

Akbar promised and went out into the open air, alive and free.

But as the days went on, he had terrible trouble with his tongue. It simply itched to tell about the king's horns. Time and time again he caught the secret just before it tripped off the end of his tongue. For several days he managed to say nothing more than, "I know something I won't tell."

Finally he had such an urge to speak the secret that he went out into the mountain wilderness where nobody ever went except the shepherds with their flocks. He looked north, south, east, west. There was nobody in sight. Even so, he was not going to take the chance of breathing the king's secret onto the open air. He knew where there was a deep hole in the ground. He was sure that his secret would be safe in that hole. So he bent over the hole and whispered through the bushes that grew at its edge, "The king has two horns." Sharing his secret, even with a hole, was such a relief that he

15

whistled lightheartedly on his way back to the palace to see if the king needed a haircut.

Soon after the hole heard Akbar's secret, a shepherd, following his grazing flocks, wandered through the same mountain wilderness. "I need a new flute," thought the shepherd. "Where on this barren hillside can I find a bit of wood big enough to whittle into a flute. Ah, I see some bushes growing at the mouth of that big hole."

So over to the hole went the shepherd. He inspected all the twigs and branches till he found a piece just the right size and just the right shape to whittle for his new flute. He cut it and walked on, watching his flocks and whittling. He worked carefully and slowly. He was still whittling as he turned his flocks toward their owners' homes at the end of the day. Just before he reached the walls of the town, his flute was finished— smooth, slim, and straight. The shepherd put it to his lips to play a happy tune. Then a most amazing thing happened.

Instead of playing what the shepherd thought he was blowing, the flute played a tune of its own. What is even more surprising, the tune had words. The bush at the mouth of the hole had had a secret too exciting to keep. As the shepherd played, the flute made from the bush shrilled so that all could hear, "The king has two horns!" The tune trilled up and down, now fast now slow; but the words were always the same, "The king has two horns! The king has two horns!" In fear, the shepherd snapped the bewitched flute in two and threw it away, but the song had been heard.

The news buzzed from man to man and from street to street till it reached the king hidden in the most private room of his palace, alone with Akbar, who was cutting his hair. And nobody who hears this story need be told what the poor barber learned at last. There is never, *never*, NEVER a time or a place that a person can let his tongue disobey him.

This folk tale was heard in Iran. It has its Greek counterpart in the legend of King Midas and the donkey ears, told in Bulfinch's *Mythology*.

THE HEN, THE MOUSE,
AND THE RABBIT

A PERSIAN FABLE

In a little house near the edge of a village there lived three friends—a hen, a mouse, and a rabbit. They lived happily together for the best of reasons. Each had his own special work which he did every day without any fuss or complaining.

The rabbit cooked the meals. The hen went daily to the forest to gather firewood. And the mouse went every day to the brook to bring the water for cooking. None ever forgot to do his own work. None ever complained. It is no wonder that the three friends lived contentedly in their little house at the edge of the village.

But one day when the hen was fluttering busily toward the forest, a dark shadow flew over her. With a hoarse "Caw," a big black crow landed in her path.

"What are you doing here?" croaked Crow.

"I'm on my way to the forest to get the wood so Rabbit can cook tomorrow's dinner," clucked Hen. "I go every day."

"Why?" grated Crow. "That's too hard work for a delicate bird like you. Why don't your lazy friends, Mouse and Rabbit, do a bit of work once in a while?"

"Oh, they do!" cackled Hen, ruffling her feathers indignantly. "Each of us has a special job that we do every day. Mouse brings water. It's a good job for her because she can swim so well that it would not matter if she did fall in the water. Rabbit cooks the meals. That's a good job for her

17

because of her long strong legs for reaching and moving things about. And I bring the firewood. That's a good job for me because I can fly up into the treetops if Wolf or any other dangerous animal comes around."

"Caw," laughed Crow. "Your fine friends have surely tricked you into being their slave. They scarcely work at all, while you kill yourself working for them."

Then Crow flew away, croaking with laughter—but Hen could not rid herself of Crow's black shadow. As she hunted for faggots in the woods, she did not cluck happily or take fluttering dance steps as she usually did. Instead, feeling terribly sorry for herself, she clumped silently under the trees. She never had realized before that she was working herself to the bone to feed a lazy mouse and a lazier rabbit. What was their easy work compared to her daily drudgery? By the time Hen reached home with a few faggots for the fire, she had worked herself into a fine rage.

"I do the hardest work every day," she clucked angrily to Mouse and Rabbit. "Let one of you do it for a change."

And suddenly Rabbit and Mouse began to feel sorry for themselves also.

"I slave over a hot stove every day of my life," gloomed Rabbit, "while you two go flitting gaily about under the clear blue sky. We can't trade jobs fast enough to suit me."

"Me too," squealed Mouse. "My back's near broken tugging heavy water from the brook. It's about time I rested in one of your soft jobs."

So the very next day the three cross and discontented creatures, who used to be friends, did change jobs. Rabbit started off to the forest to fetch firewood for tomorrow's fire. Hen went to the brook to bring water. Mouse stayed home—perched on the edge of the big kettle to stir the stew.

Do you think they were all happy because they had new work in the place of the jobs that were really and truly their own? Let's see—

Rabbit, trying very hard to feel gay and carefree, went

hopping off into the woods. While she was hunting for faggots, a big gray wolf stalked slowly up behind her. Rabbit did not have wings to fly into the treetops as Hen would have done. Rabbit could take long leaps—but so could Wolf. And that is why Rabbit never went back to the little house at the edge of the village.

Meanwhile, Hen, thinking what a short walk it was from their house, went fluttering off toward the brook. Reaching the brook, Hen gripped the pail with her claws and dipped it into the water. The rushing brook filled the pail and carried it downstream as Hen clawed frantically at the handle. Hen had never stepped in water above her toenails before. She had no more idea of swimming than Rabbit had of flying. And this is why Hen never went back to the little house at the edge of the village.

While all this was happening, Mouse was at home cooking dinner. She was safe enough sitting on the edge of the kettle to stir the stew. Her trouble came when it was necessary to lift the kettle from the fire. She did not have long strong arms like Rabbit's. Mouse tugged and she pushed, but the kettle was too heavy for her. In her struggle to move it, she lost her balance and fell into the fire. And this is why Mouse never knew that Rabbit did not come home from the forest. It is why Mouse never knew that Hen did not come home from the brook.

Of course, this is only a fable that the Persians have told their children for many years. At the end of the story, they always look very solemn and say, "And that happened because the three friends were not satisfied, each with the work that was really her own."

This fable was heard in Iran. It was told by a young man who remembered it from a school reading book.

THE LOST SONG

A LEGEND OF THE AMERICAN INDIANS

"What song is that, mother?"

The Indian girl gazed over the wide Potomac. She peered searchingly into the forest.

"Do you mean the song of the cardinal?" The Indian mother was watching a flame of red on the oak branch above them.

"Not the cardinal, mother."

"Do you mean the music of the mighty Potomac?"

"Not the river, mother."

"Do you mean the song of the wind in the forest?"

"Not the wind through the trees and the vines."

The Indian mother looked thoughtfully at her daughter. Was the child old enough to understand? "Daughter, you are hearing the song of all things. It is the song of a world that lives in peace and harmony under the smile of the Great Spirit. The birds in the treetops, the waves on the beach, the wind in the forest, the insects in the grass, the crackling campfires, the friendly voices of the people, the wild animals in the woods, even the sun and moon and stars—all join together to sing the most beautiful song in the world. It is soft and sweet in the morning, full and clear at noon. It is a lullaby in the evening, a humming murmur at night. It is the praise and joy of a world at peace. You and I can join in the song."

Singing together, the mother and the little girl turned from the banks of the restless Potomac to walk swiftly along the trail that followed the brook back to their village. They passed a group of men sitting about a campfire and talking in low tones. A look of dread crossed the mother's face. There was a sound in those voices which she had never heard before, the gloating of men who were trying to get the better of some-one. But there was no enemy! Why that cruel note? It did not go well with the song of all things.

"Okee, the Evil One, is whispering to them," sighed the Indian mother.

As the days passed, things grew more and more strange in the little village. The men gathered daily in groups. They boiled roots, bark, clay, and leaves to make paint for their faces. They made new bows and arrows, sharper and stronger than those they used for hunting the white-tailed deer. They made many tomahawks and practiced throwing them.

The song of all things grew dim and wistful. The men were too busy to listen to it. The women and children could still hear it, but it was not full and clear as in the happy, carefree times.

One day the men covered their faces and their bodies with gruesome painting. They picked up their bows and arrows and their tomahawks. "We are off on our hunting trip," they shouted to their wives and children. "We will bring back treasure."

The women and the children trembled as the men filed noiselessly off through the woods. The families left behind had never heard of war or hatred, but they could feel both now. The song of all things was silent. Not even the gentlest woman or the gayest child could catch an echo of it. The years went on. Battle cries and the screams of captured peo-ple were heard on the shores of the little brooks flowing into the wide Potomac, but never the song of all things. War and hatred had killed it.

Kiwassa, the Great Spirit, pitied his people because they had lost their song. Those who talked much with the Great Spirit said that some day the song would be found again. It would be found by one of them who was nobler, braver, kinder than all the rest. Year after year went by. But none could hear the lost song.

21

One day, when the little Indian girl had grown to be a beautiful young woman, the village by the little creek flowing into the great Potomac was captured. The conquering tribe was led by a tall young chieftain of great courage. Strong warrior that he was, his face held a strange kindness on those days when he was not on the warpath. He made friends with the people of the conquered tribe. He sat beside their campfire and talked with them of many things.

But he carried this friendship too far, so thought his own tribesmen, when he chose a wife from the conquered tribe—the Indian maiden with the song of all things still hidden in her heart.

"You must choose a wife of your own people!" his warriors demanded. But the young chieftain refused.

Then his men secretly sharpened their tomahawks. They caught their chieftain unprepared for their attack. They tied him and the Indian girl to a stake. They heaped dry branches and bark around it. They brought fire and lighted the pile.

As the fire began to crackle under them, the girl and the chieftain talked together.

"Have you ever heard the song of all things?" she asked.

"When I was a lad, I heard it," he answered. "It went sweeping through the valleys and climbing over the hills. It was soft and low on the dark days. On the sunny days it swelled loud and sweet. It had a wistful lilt on the rainy days. When the moon was full, it sang a song of mystery and wonder. It sang a song of faith and hope when the trees were bare in the winter, and a song of victory and joy when the springtime brought the green back to the meadows and the woodlands."

The flames crept nearer.

"When I saw the light in your eyes, I thought that perhaps you would be the one to bring the lost song back to the world," said the Indian maiden.

"I was one of those who kept it silent. I was a warrior," said the young chieftain sadly. "Kiwassa, the Great Spirit, has

22

said that the lost song will be found only by someone who is great enough to stop battles and hatred."

"You might have been that one," sighed the maiden. The flames had caught her deerskin dress. Her muscles tightened, but her eyes never left the face of the young chieftain.

"Since I have seen you," said the young chieftain, "I feel that the lost song is somewhere near. I am sorry that I ever killed, that I ever fought or conquered. War is terrible. Hatred is of Okee, the Evil One. Love is of Kiwassa, the Great Spirit."

The flames were rising higher. The Indian maiden lifted her eyes toward the blue sky above the tops of the oak trees.

"O Kiwassa, Great Spirit," she cried. "Give him another chance. He has almost found the secret of the lost song. Let him try again."

Kiwassa, the Great Spirit, heard the prayer of the Indian maiden.

The young chieftain was changed into a gray bird with a long restless tail and a throat made for melody. Kiwassa told him that he could fly over all the world with power to copy all the songs that he heard. He was to try one song after another, to piece together different melodies in the hope of once again finding the song of all things in a world of peace.

For many years the young chieftain in the body of the mockingbird has been flying about the world. He flies north, south, east, and west, ever learning new songs, ever repeating and combining them. He has sung as many different tunes as there are minutes in a year, but still he has not found the lost song. When he finds a song of breath-taking beauty, a dark little undertone is sure to creep in—the mutterings of men with tomahawks.

Some day the battle cries will be stilled. Then once again the lost song will go swelling through the valleys and soaring over the hilltops. Once again the mockingbird will learn the song of all things and will teach it to a world that is at peace.

A TALL TALE GROWS SHORT

A TURKISH FOLK TALE

Here is the story that the people of Turkey tell when they
wish a boaster to know he is making a monkey of himself

Nasr-ed-Din Hodja was bored by boasting—by other people's boasting. Take this fellow from Persia, for instance. Ever
since the Hodja came into the coffeehouse an hour ago,
ready for a good chat with old friends, he had heard nothing
but the voice of this stranger from Persia. On and on went
the voice—boasting, boasting, boasting.

Some of the coffeehouse sitters were stupid enough to
keep the tiresome man talking by asking questions. But not
the Hodja! If that braggart ever stopped talking long enough,
the Hodja was going to take over. If one man was going to
do all the talking, it might as well be the Hodja as that
stranger from Persia. The Hodja could tell wonderful tales
too. Listen to that Persian windbag now!

"You would never believe your eyes if you saw our palace!"
the man was saying. "It has hundreds of rooms, so many that
you would lose your way in its halls and on its stairways.
The walls are made of glistening white marble, inlaid with
designs done in precious stones. The greatest artists of the
world have toiled over these mosaics. The palace gardens are
full of rare flowers and trees collected from far countries. The
gardens alone are bigger than all the vineyards of this plain put
together. The palace itself covers as much ground as your
whole city of Ak Shehir."

This was too much for Nasr-ed-Din Hodja. Luckily, the
Persian guest took time off to drink another cup of sweet

black coffee. Being a well-mannered foreigner, he drank noisily to show that he liked the coffee. He smacked his lips. It took not quite a minute; but when he set his cup down to continue his story, he found that the Hodja had taken his place as the teller of travelers' tales.

"That reminds me of the time I visited our Turkish palace at Bursa." The Hodja jumped to his feet, the better to tell his story. "What a building! Big? If anyone else told you, you would never believe."

The Hodja had to raise his voice to talk above the noises outside. A rattling wagon had driven up with the flourish that drivers put on at the end of a long journey. There was loud arguing about the price between traveler and driver. There was the neighing of horses who smelled a stable and food. There was the jingle of harness charms and decorations. Some men left their tables to look out the door to see who was arriving, but not the Hodja. His voice boomed above all the noise.

"You would never believe anyone else about that palace at Bursa. Its length is every bit of eight thousand feet," yelled the Hodja. He paused for a bit to let this information impress his listeners before he went on. "And the width of the palace at Bursa—"

Just then the door opened and in walked Siraj-ed-Din Bey, just back from Bursa, where he had been a guest at the palace. Every man in Ak Shehir had heard about the trip. Nasr-ed-Din Hodja looked at Siraj-ed-Din Bey and gulped.

"And the width of the palace," squeaked the Hodja in a weak, small voice, "is about fifty feet."

"A strange shape for a palace," said the Persian. "A very strange shape, indeed. You say it is eight thousand feet one way and fifty feet another? That is not a palace, my good friend. That is nothing but a long hall."

"I could have built you a palace of better shape," began the Hodja, "if I had started a few minutes earlier. Its shape was all spoiled by—" The Hodja did not finish his sentence, but he looked reproachfully at Siraj-ed-Din Bey, who was sitting now at a table near the center of the coffeehouse.

Then a very meek and quiet Hodja busied himself with his small cup of sweet black coffee. The men of Ak Shehir understood why the palace had suddenly become so narrow, but the traveler from Persia never did understand.

THE COW THAT COUNTED SEVEN

A STORY FROM THE MIDRASH

Long ago in the East there lived a Jewish farmer who obeyed well the commandments of his faith. So careful was he to "remember the sabbath day, to keep it holy" that every member of his household and of his barnyard kept the commandment with him. No one was more obedient to this law than his faithful cow who dragged his wooden plow in the spring and autumn, trod his threshing floor in late summer, pulled his loads whenever he bade her, and gave him a few cups of milk each day.

In fact, this small brown cow seemed able to count to seven, so well did she know when the day of rest had come. On the first day of the week she stood patiently while the yoke was placed on her so that she could pull the forked stick as her master held it to turn a shallow furrow in the hard soil. On the second day of the week she dragged the plow through the early morning and the late afternoon, and stopped only when her master needed to catch his breath or wipe the sweat from his forehead. On the third day of the week she plodded patiently back and forth across the big field outside the village where her master's flat-roofed house snuggled among its neighbors. Thus she worked through the fourth day, the fifth day, and the sixth day. But when the seventh day of the week came, she lay quietly beside her pile of straw, chewed her cud, switched away the flies, and never thought of pulling a plow or dragging the weighted board about the threshing floor.

Nobody was quite sure how the cow knew. Perhaps inside

27

the cow there was a sort of calendar that ticked off each day—one, two, three, four, five, six—till it came to the seventh day of rest. Or perhaps the cow recognized the sabbath stillness that came with the evening candles, the singing of psalms, and the quiet peace that filled every village home where the Jewish laws were obeyed.

Unfortunately, her master became so poor that he could no longer afford to keep her. His poverty made him sell her to the highest bidder, even though the new owner was a man who laughed at the Jewish laws and at the Jewish faith in one great God.

Now it happened to be the middle of a week in the threshing season when the sale was made. On the first, the second, and the third days of the week, the small brown cow walked uncomplainingly round and round her old master's threshing floor, and tugged behind her the wooden drag on which her master sat. Each time round the threshing floor separated more of the grain from its hulls. The farmer's wife and son picked up the wheat by the forkful, and let the wind blow away the chaff while the good grain fell to the ground. They worked fast, hoping to finish before the cow must be led away to its new owner.

On the evening of the third day of the week, the sad farmer led his faithful cow to the neighbor, to the man who laughed at the law of the Jews and at the God of the Jews.

"I know she will work well for you," the farmer said, as he gave her a last pat and accepted the handful of money which he needed so badly.

On the fourth day of the week the small brown cow pulled her new master round and round his threshing floor. On the fifth day of the week she obeyed every word he spoke to her. On the sixth day of the week she worked so well that her new master thought there was no farmer in the village so fortunate as he.

But on the seventh day of the week, when the feeling of peace and worship flowed from every home where Jewish laws were honored, the small brown cow lay placidly beside her pile of straw, chewed her cud, and switched away the flies. As you know, there is nothing in the world more serene than a cow who intends to spend her day resting and enjoying herself.

Her new master shouted at her, but she flicked not even an ear. He poked at her, but she did not twitch a muscle. He tried to force the yoke over her head, but she brushed him away as calmly as she switched away the pestering flies. Her new master ran to her old master's house and found him starting with his family for the sabbath worship at the synagogue.

"The cow you sold me is lazy and disobedient," the new owner shouted to the old. "Come with me! Make her get up and work!"

"She knows it is the sabbath," answered the old master. "I must explain to her that she must live now as her new owner lives."

With these words, he went to the small brown cow and whispered in her ear. Looking as sad as a cow can look, she gave a little shiver, then stood up, and bent her head meekly for the binding on of the yoke.

But no yoke did she feel! Her new master stood speechless beside her. First he stared at the cow. Then he stared at the farmer whose voice she obeyed.

"That cow cannot reason," said the man who laughed at Jewish law, "but still she feels the need to rest on the seventh day. I can reason. Why shouldn't I be as wise as the cow?"

Then he gave the cow a pat and followed his neighbor to the synagogue to find out more about the God who said:

Remember the sabbath day, to keep it holy. Six days you shall labor, and do all your work; but the seventh day is a sabbath to the Lord your God; in it you shall not do any work, you, or your son, or your daughter, your manservant, or your maidservant, or your cattle, or the sojourner who is within your gates; for in six days the Lord made heaven and earth, the sea, and all that is in them, and rested the seventh day; therefore the Lord blessed the sabbath day and hallowed it.

—Exod. 20:8-11

He liked what he learned.

And when the new owner of the small brown cow joined the Jewish faith and promised to obey the Jewish laws, he took a new Jewish name. It was Hanina ben Turta, which means Hanina the Son of a Cow.

Retold from Midrash 'Aseret ha-Dibrot, the Midrash of the Ten Commandments.

SONGS FROM THE OLD TESTAMENT

THE SONG OF THE WELL

Enan could not remember way back to the days when he was a baby living by the River Nile in Egypt. His mother used to tell stories about that land—green and fertile because of the flowing river. But to Enan the world was nothing but desert, miles and miles of parched desert to be crossed before he and the other Israelites reached their Promised Land of Canaan. Enan tried to have faith in their leader Moses and in the God that Moses said was showing them the way to the beautiful land of Canaan. But day after day Enan saw nothing but bare rocks, hard brown soil, blowing sand, and a few thirsty weeds.

He knew what it meant when the men traveling at the front of the caravan suddenly began to sing a special song. They had just reached a spot of high land that gave a view of the plain that lay ahead. The men danced in a circle as they sang this glad song:

> Spring up, O well!—Sing to it!—
> the well which the princes dug,
> which the nobles of the people delved,
> with the scepter and with their staves.
> —Num. 21:17-18

Enan ran ahead to join the singing and the dancing. He knew what he would see over the rise in the ground. He would see a green oasis in the desert. Yes, there it was—a patch of green grass, a few palm trees, some bushes, two gazelles grazing. The water did not show, but the greenness proved it was there.

Enan ran with the men who hurried ahead to find the water.

With their staves they dug in the ground till the spring spurted up. They walled the spring with rocks so that it would make a well where the women could let down their jars to draw water. Enan knew that soon they would pitch their black tents around the spring and rest there before starting the next hot stretch of their long journey. But before the tents were pitched, the Israelites sang again the old song of their people about God's great gift of living water, "Spring up, O well!"

The desert years made the Hebrew people grateful for the gift of water. Wells, springs, and rivers are mentioned often in their stories, in their prophecies, and in their songs praising God for his care. To this day, water is looked upon as a wonderful thing in the countries of the Middle East. Improving the water supply is one of the most important things that engineers from the United Nations are doing today to help the people of Bible lands. We who live in a country where water comes to us easily can learn from the ancient Hebrews how to thank God for his great gift of water.

> Thou visitest the earth and waterest it,
>   thou greatly enrichest it;
> the river of God is full of water;
>   thou providest their grain,
>   for so thou hast prepared it.
> Thou waterest its furrows abundantly,
>   settling its ridges,
> softening it with showers,
>   and blessing its growth.
> Thou crownest the year with thy bounty;
>   the tracks of thy chariot drip with fatness.
> The pastures of the wilderness drip,
>   the hills gird themselves with joy,
> the meadows clothe themselves with flocks,
>   the valleys deck themselves with grain,
>   they shout and sing together for joy.
>   —Ps. 65:9-13

A FARMER'S SONG

"Abihu! Abihu, my son!" called the shepherd.

There was no answer. Abihu's mother looked up from grinding the corn. "I think he has gone to the market place to watch the potter."

"Abihu does anything but his own work," grumbled the father. "I believe he wishes he had been born a potter's son!" And the shepherd went stumping off toward the market place.

At the potter's shop he found Abihu watching a lump of clay whirring on the wheel as the potter's skillful fingers molded it into an earthen jar.

"Abihu," said the shepherd. "You know it is your turn to watch the flocks. Go—and tell your brother that he may come home to rest."

Dragging his feet and looking backward at the whirring wheel of the potter, Abihu made his way slowly home. He took the bread and cheese his mother had ready for him and then walked slowly along the path that followed a valley out to the open hillside where goats and sheep were grazing. He settled down on the hard ground beside his older brother Asher.

"Why so glum?" Asher put his shepherd's flute to his lips to play a cheerful tune.

"I don't see the sense of always tending these stupid sheep and goats," said Abihu grumpily. "I should think they could take care of themselves. They are more trouble than they are worth."

Asher played his flute till he found a tune that pleased him. Then he laid down his flute and sang an old song of his people:

Know well the condition of your flocks,
  and give attention to your herds;
for riches do not last for ever;
  and does a crown endure to all generations?
When the grass is gone, and the new growth appears,
  and the herbage of the mountains is gathered,
the lambs will provide your clothing,
  and the goats the price of a field;
there will be enough goats' milk for your food,
  for the food of your household.

—Prov. 27:23-27

Then Asher handed the flute and the shepherd's staff to
Abihu. He walked down the hillside toward the path that
led through the valley to the village. As he walked, he heard
the reedy sound of the flute. Abihu was playing the old, old
song of his people "Know well the condition of your flocks."
Asher smiled to himself and sang with the thin melody of the
flute.

A SONG OF WORSHIP

His name, Habakkuk, is all we know about him—his name and the few pages in the Old Testament written by him. From those few pages we learn that he was a prophet, probably one of the prophets that stayed around the great temple in Jerusalem. We learn also that he lived in the days when his own Hebrew people were doing many things that were very wrong. He lived in the days when "that bitter and hasty nation," Chaldea, was marching "through the breadth of the earth, to seize habitations not their own." That dates Habakkuk about six hundred years before Jesus was born.

And why do we care about Habakkuk? There are two reasons. First, Habakkuk gave us the words which are used all over the world when people come together, in churches or in church schools, to worship God. Sometimes we speak this call to worship. Sometimes we sing it. Always it reminds us that God is very near.

> The Lord is in his holy temple;
>   let all the earth keep silence before him.
>   —Hab. 2:20

Second, Habakkuk was the first man to put in writing the question that men and women, boys and girls, have asked and are asking today: "Why does God let bad things happen to good people?" Moreover, Habakkuk shares with us the answer that God gave to him when he stood alone on his watchtower and talked with God about the problem of good people having trouble while some bad people seemed to be getting along quite comfortably. Habakkuk's familiar call to worship is part of his answer to the question: "Why does God let bad things happen to good people?"

You have wondered why innocent children in Korea or Indo-China lost their homes and their families because of a war that was not their fault. You have wondered why some friend of yours was hurt by sickness or accident or a hurricane. You have wondered why someone you loved had to die. You may have wondered why you seemed to get a bad break yourself when you were really trying to do the right thing. You may have asked, "Why does God let such things happen?" Then you can understand how Habakkuk felt when he said:

> O Lord, how long shall I cry for help,
>   and thou wilt not hear?
> Or cry to thee "Violence!"
>   and thou wilt not save?
> Why dost thou make me see wrongs
>   and look upon trouble?
>
> —Hab. 1:2-3

Habakkuk goes on to describe the wickedness, unfairness, and unhappiness that he saw on every side. He asks how God, who is good, can allow such things.

> Thou who art of purer eyes than to behold evil
>   and canst not look on wrong,
> why dost thou look on faithless men,
>   and art silent when the wicked swallows up
>   the man more righteous than he?
>
> —Hab. 1:13

Then Habakkuk climbed up into his tower where he could not be disturbed while he waited for God's answer to his questions. When the answer came, God told Habakkuk to write it on tablets so plainly that a person could read it even while he was running. It was quite a long answer, but it boils down to this: "Be patient. It may take a long time, but God's good way will win out in the end. It is not necessary for you to know when or why. You just keep on calmly and faithfully doing what you know is right. Do not fret or worry about what you can not understand. Good people live by their faithfulness."

Then Habakkuk felt better. He looked around again at the wickedness, unhappiness, and unfairness; but he had the faith that in the long run God's good way would win. He knew now that his job was to steadfastly do his best in the place where God had given him work to do. Habakkuk felt calm and peaceful and full of faith in God. He was ready to say the words which we still use as our call to worship. He knew that there was wrong in the world—

> But the Lord is in his holy temple;
> let all the earth keep silence before him.

A SONG OF GOD'S STEADFAST LOVE

When King David set up his tent church, called the tabernacle, he chose men to bring the ark of God into it. You remember how the Israelites thought that God was really inside the beautiful box they called his ark. David chose some men who could play musical instruments and others who could sing well. He chose some to carry the ark into the tent and others to stand guard at the door. And as the ark was placed inside the tabernacle, the harps and cymbals played while the singers sang a long song of thanksgiving ending with the words:

> O give thanks to the Lord, for he is good;
> for his steadfast love endures for ever!
> —I Chr. 16:34

We find this hymn again when David's son Solomon dedicated the beautiful temple which he and his subjects had built in Jerusalem for the worship of God. The priests carried the ark of God from its old place in the tabernacle to the holy of holies in the temple. Then there was a flourish of music and a hymn of thanksgiving ending with the words:

> For he is good,
> for his steadfast love endures for ever.
> —II Chr. 5:13

We read the hymn again in the book of Jeremiah. Nebuchadrezzar, king of Babylon, had marched against the Israelites. Everything that they loved seemed to be lost as they were driven off into exile in Babylon. Even their beauti-

40

ful temple at Jerusalem was captured and destroyed. The prophet Jeremiah tried to comfort the Israelites by saying that God would bring them back to Jerusalem. Jeremiah said:

There shall be heard again the voice of mirth and the voice of gladness . . . the voices of those who sing, as they bring thank offerings to the house of the Lord:

> "Give thanks to the Lord of hosts,
>   for the Lord is good,
>   for his steadfast love endures for ever!"
> —Jer. 33:11

In the book of Ezra we find Jeremiah's prophecy coming true. Jerusalem was freed. The Israelites returned home. First they built an altar and worshiped God. Then they laid the foundations to rebuild their temple.

And when the builders laid the foundation of the temple of the Lord, the priests in their vestments came forward with trumpets, and the Levites, the sons of Asaph, with cymbals, to praise the Lord, according to the directions of David king of Israel; and they sang responsively, praising and giving thanks to the Lord,
> "For he is good,
>   for his steadfast love endures for ever toward Israel."
> —Ezra 3:10, 11

Even today we bring offerings and praise God. We could praise him in the same words that were taught by David so long ago.

Instead of being a single story, the above is the outline of four stories which can be found in vivid detail in the Bible.

A SONG OF GIVING

About a thousand years before Jesus was born, there lived
in Jerusalem a king named David. This king had two great
wishes. First, he hoped to unite the Hebrew people into one
strong nation. And that he did. Second, he wanted to build
a beautiful house of cedar where God could be worshiped.
And to that God said, "No!"

"There is an old proverb in the East: "When God closes one
door, he opens a thousand other doors." David could not
build the beautiful temple for God, but he could help someone
else build it. While he was gathering materials for the temple,
King David said a few words that have helped thousands of
people for thousands of years. Probably you have sung these
words yourself, in church or in church school, without knowing that they were first said by King David about three
thousand years ago. See if you can recognize these words
when they come in the story.

Still thinking of that beautiful temple that should be built
for the worship of God, David called together in Jerusalem
the chief men of the kingdom. His own sons were there, of
course. So were the head men of all the tribes of Israel, the
army officers that were in charge of the divisions that had
fought for their king, the stewards who looked after the
royal property, the officials who kept things in order about
the palace, the mightiest warriors, and many other important
men of the kingdom.

King David greeted them:

Hear me, my brethren and my people. I had it in my heart to
build a house of rest for the ark of the covenant of the Lord, and

42

for the footstool of our God; and I made preparations for building. But God said to me, "You may not build a house for my name, for you are a warrior and have shed blood." . . . He said to me, "It is Solomon your son who shall build my house and my courts."

—I Chr. 28:2-3, 6

Then King David called Prince Solomon forward and said to him:

You, Solomon my son, know the God of your father, and serve him with a whole heart and with a willing mind. . . . Take heed now, for the Lord has chosen you to build a house for the sanctuary; be strong, and do it.

—I Chr. 28:9, 10

Being a good father, David did not leave Solomon to do it alone. He passed on to his son the plans he had made for the temple. They were careful plans, such as an architect might make. They gave the names and the sizes of the rooms and of the courts. They told where to build with cedar and where to use silver, gold, iron, bronze, or precious stones. The plans were in writing so that there would be no forgetting and no mistakes.

Being a good ruler, as well as a good father, King David was able to tell Solomon about the many men of the kingdom who would help:

And with you in all the work will be every willing man who has skill for any kind of service; also the officers and all the people will be wholly at your command.

—I Chr. 28:21

Being a good provider, as well as a good ruler and a good father, David told Solomon and the assembled people about the quantities of precious material he had already amassed for the building of this house of God:

I have provided for the house of my God, so far as I was able, the gold for the things of gold, the silver for the things of silver,

43

and the bronze for the things of bronze, the iron for the things of iron, and wood for the things of wood, besides great quantities of onyx and stones for setting, antimony, colored stones, all sorts of precious stones, and marble.

—I Chr. 29:2

Then he said that, in addition to these things, he had treasure of his own which he was giving. After describing this treasure, he asked a question.

Who then will offer willingly, consecrating himself today to the Lord?

—I Chr. 29:5

At this question the people came forward with their offerings. The heads of families came and the leaders of tribes and the army officers and the men who managed the king's household. They brought gold and silver, bronze and iron, precious stones. And they all "rejoiced because . . . they had offered freely to the Lord; David the king also rejoiced greatly."

Glad with the people, David bowed his head in prayer to consecrate their gifts. And as David talked with God about the gifts they were all bringing, he remembered something important. He remembered that a few years ago he himself was only a shepherd boy. He remembered how recently his great army and multitude of followers were only scattered tribes fearing strong enemies. He realized that neither he nor his people had created the gold and silver and iron and bronze that they were giving to God. All these things had come from the good earth that God had given them. He was thinking humbly of these things as he prayed:

Thine, O Lord, is the greatness, and the power, and the glory, and the victory, and the majesty; for all that is in the heavens and in the earth is thine. . . . Both riches and honor come from thee, and thou rulest over all. . . .

But who am I, and what is my people, that we should be able

44

thus to offer willingly? For all things come from thee, and of thy own have we given thee. . . . O Lord our God, all this abundance that we have provided for building thee a house for thy holy name comes from thy hand and is all thy own.

—I Chr. 29:11, 12, 14, 16

Did you notice in David's prayer some words that we say or sing when we bring gifts to God? We remember that we are not giving to God something that we created ourselves. We are giving him a tiny part of the great gifts that he has given us. That is why we feel humble and grateful when we bring our offerings and sing:

> All things come of Thee, O Lord,
> And of Thine own have we given Thee.

The last quotation is given in the King James Version as contained in hymnals.

SONGS OF A NEW KING

One of the oldest, perhaps *the* oldest, Christmas picture is near Rome. It was painted about two hundred years after Jesus was born. To see this picture you would have to ride north out of Rome to the catacomb of Priscilla, an ancient cemetery under the ground. It is a network of tunnels and underground rooms high enough for a tall man to stand erect. To enter the catacomb, you would carry a candle downstairs into a tunnel and then follow your guide through many turns that lead through rooms with paintings on walls and ceilings. The dim lamps and your own candle would light up the pictures which give beauty to the ancient underground cemetery, as flowers and trees and statues give beauty to our cemeteries.

You would recognize the Christmas picture as soon as you tipped your head back and saw it painted on the ceiling—a star, and below the star a mother holding a baby in her lap. Beside the mother you would see the picture of a man holding a scroll of paper in one hand and gesturing with the other. Of course you would know right away that the mother was Mary and that the Baby was Jesus. The star would tell you that. But you might have trouble guessing the name of the man. If he were a shepherd come to adore Jesus, he should have a staff or a lamb in his hand instead of a scroll. If he were one of the wise men from the East, he should be carrying a gift of gold or frankincense or myrrh—not a rolled-up piece of paper. If you guessed Joseph, you would have to think of why the artist would paint his picture with a scroll in his hand. Joseph was a carpenter, not a scholar.

When this picture was discovered, its artist had been dead

at least sixteen hundred years. There was nobody to give the name of the man with the scroll in his hand. Scholars put their heads together and kept guessing until someone had an idea which they all thought was correct. They decided that the man in the picture was the Old Testament prophet Isaiah, who had written so many years ago that some day a child would be born who would grow up to be the sort of man that Jesus became. The scholars said that the artist was showing Isaiah rejoicing that the Baby he had prophesied had been born. They said that Isaiah was holding in one hand the scroll on which he wrote about the coming of Jesus, and that he was gesturing with the other hand while he talked with Mary about her wonderful Baby. You have heard some of the words that were written on Isaiah's scroll:

> For to us a child is born,
>   to us a son is given;
> and the government will be upon his shoulder,
>   and his name will be called
> "Wonderful Counselor, Mighty God,
>   Everlasting Father, Prince of Peace."
>
> —Isa. 9:6

There are parts in Isaiah that tell of the coming of the Messiah. One begins:

> Behold, a king will reign in righteousness,
>   and princes will rule in justice.
>
> —Isa. 32:1

Then it goes on with words that you cannot readily appreciate unless you understand about the barren, treeless wilderness which Isaiah knew. Imagine that the sun is blistering hot. Imagine that the wind is blowing the dust and the sand. A twisting tornado lifts up some dirt and whirls it round and round as it makes its way across the desert. As far as the eye can see, there is no tree or rock to shelter you from the dust-filled wind or the burning sun. In the distance, in one direction, you can see a circular wall of hard-packed clay that someone built as a shelter. In the distance, in another direction, you can see a crooked roof of dried camel's-thorn held up by sagging sticks—another shelter built by a traveler across the wilderness. If the dry ground at your feet were not baked so hard by the sun, you would hollow out a cave to crawl in and escape from the heat and the pelting wind. You would give anything for a tree to give shade or for a rock large enough to crawl behind.

It was because Isaiah knew such parched wilderness land that he could write of the king who was coming:

> Each will be like a hiding-place from the wind,
> a covert from the tempest,
> like streams of water in a dry place,
> like the shade of a great rock in a weary land.
>
> —Isa. 32:2

It was because Isaiah was a poet that he used these things of the outdoors to describe what happens in a person's life. He was saying that as any person goes through life, he meets hard work and disappointment and temptation, which are as much of a strain as the blistering sun and the beating wind of the wilderness. He was saying that a man was coming who would give strength and comfort—"like the shade of a great rock in a weary land."

The picture of Isaiah and the Madonna is shown as Fig. 162 in *Light from the Ancient Past* by Jack Finegan (Princeton University Press, 1946).

ACROSS THE CENTURIES

THE BATTLE THAT
NEVER WAS FOUGHT

Long, long ago, when the Israelites were beginning to learn about God, they had many rules that seem strange to us today. And they were most severe to anyone who disobeyed. One of the rules went like this:

Any man of the house of Israel, or of the strangers that sojourn among them, who offers a burnt offering or sacrifice, and does not bring it to the door of the tent of meeting, to sacrifice it to the Lord; that man shall be cut off from his people.

—Lev. 17:8-9

This meant there was just one place where the Israelites were supposed to worship God by offering burnt sacrifice on an altar. That one place was the altar at the door of the tent of meeting, or tabernacle. Anyone who tried to burn a sacrifice on any other altar could expect to be severely punished. He could expect to have all the other Israelites turn against him.

Once this rule almost plunged the Israelites into a terrible battle—almost but not quite. Luckily, the leaders of the two sides of the argument had the sense to talk things over *before* instead of *after* they drew their swords to fight.

This story begins when the Israelites were on their long journey from Egypt to their Promised Land in Palestine. The men who were descended from three of Joseph's brothers—Reuben, Gad, and Manasseh—liked the level grazing land on the east side of the Jordan River.

"Must we travel further?" they asked Moses. "We like this

pasture land. We are shepherds and cattlemen and must live in this sort of country. We do not care about crossing the Jordan River. Let us settle here."

But Moses answered, "We need you men to help win the land on the other side of Jordan."

"We'll help," the men promised. "Let us first build fenced cities here for our wives and children. Let us build sheepfolds for our flocks. We will leave our families and our animals here and go with you to win the land on the west side of the Jordan River. Then let us return to this, the place where we want to make our home. We like it here."

Moses agreed. The men built their fenced cities and their sheepfolds. Then they left their wives and children, their sheep and their cattle. They crossed the Jordan River to help the other Israelites win the Promised Land. At last this was accomplished. At last the men could return to their families and their flocks on the east bank of the Jordan River.

Just before they crossed the River on their way home, they stopped and built a great altar on the west side of the Jordan— a high altar that would be easy to see from their fenced cities and their pastures on the other side of the river. When they reached home, they gathered their families about them and explained why they had built the altar.

"Look well at the altar," they told their children and their wives. "And hear why we built it. As the years go on, your cousins who live on the west side of the Jordan River may boast because they have the tabernacle in their keeping, because they have the one altar where sacrifices may be burned to the honor of God. They may say: 'The tabernacle is with us. You have nothing to do with the Lord God.' If they ever say that to you, point at this altar which your fathers have built as a reminder that we and you and your children are the children of the Lord our God, as well as they. We cannot often visit the tabernacle of the Lord God at Shiloh to offer our sacrifices, but we can always look at this high altar and remember that God is with us on this side of the Jordan."

To us who know that God is everywhere the altar does not seem so important, but we must remember that these Israelites of long ago were just beginning to learn about God. As they went about their work or their play, they would look often across the river and feel pride in the altar that reminded them that God was with them in their new home.

Suddenly there came across the river a group of stern-looking men. The fathers recognized the leaders—Phinehas the priest's son and the ten princes who led the ten tribes of Israelites that were settling on the west side of the Jordan. The fathers started to greet the visitors as cousins and old comrades, but—

"All the Israelites on the west of Jordan are angry with you!" the visitors announced. "We are going to wage war against you!"

"War—against—us? What have we done? We thought we were your friends," said the men of the tribes of Reuben, Gad, and Manasseh.

"You have sinned against God!" said Phinehas.

"Sinned—against—God?"

"You know as well as we that the altar of the tabernacle at Shiloh is the one and only place to offer sacrifices to the Lord God."

"We know," agreed the men.

"Then *why* did you build an altar on the banks of the Jordan?"

"Oh, the altar by the Jordan—" began the men, but Phinehas interrupted.

"You are no better than the heathen who offer sacrifices to their heathen gods," scolded Phinehas. "It is a sin to burn sacrifices anywhere but on the one altar that stands before the tabernacle at Shiloh. That is why we have come to warn you that all the other Israelites are going to wage war against you."

"Oh, we never planned to burn sacrifices on that altar," said the descendants of Reuben, Gad, and Manasseh. "We built the altar as a reminder that God is with us. We feared that in time to come your children might say to our children, 'What have you to do with the Lord God of Israel? Because the Lord has made the Jordan a boundary between us and you, you have no part in the Lord.' We were afraid that your children would make our children feel they did not belong to God. We built this altar as a reminder that we, on this side of the Jordan, trust in the one true God."

Phinehas and the ten princes looked at each other. For a minute they could think of nothing to say. Then they began to smile in a relieved sort of way. They were glad not to have to fight after all.

Phinehas spoke slowly: "God is with us all."

There was not another word about waging a war. There was no need to fight, because the two sides had taken the trouble to talk over what they did not understand.

Retold from Num. 32; Lev. 17:8-9; Josh. 22.

A LUNCH THAT GREW

"Give me a ride, Ezekias?" A very small boy looked admiringly at the boy on the little gray donkey.

"No," said Ezekias, "I am in a hurry. I want to catch up with that crowd of people. See! They are following the Teacher named Jesus."

"Oh!" The very small boy watched wistfully as Ezekias and the donkey bobbed along the path and overtook a group of trudging children.

"Give us a turn on the donkey?" begged the boys and girls.

Ezekias shook his head. "I'm catching up with the people who are going up the mountain."

"That's where we are going, too," said one of the children, looking hopefully at the donkey.

"If we took turns on the donkey, we could all go faster," said another.

Ezekias shook his head.

"If the little ones rode, we could all walk quickly together," said a girl whose very small sister was dragging on her hand.

Ezekias clucked to his donkey, whose hoofs scattered dust on the disappointed children. After all, it was his father's donkey, wasn't it? It wasn't his fault that their fathers would not furnish donkeys for them to ride, was it? He tried not to hear what the others were saying about boys who were never willing to share what they had.

The little donkey's trot was brisk. In a few minutes he carried Ezekias to the mountain top. People were gathering from all sides, from Ezekias' village and from villages farther away. Some came on foot and some on donkeyback. Hundreds of people! Thousands of people! They crowded closer and closer to the Teacher. They did not care that he had come to the mountain top with a few of his closest friends to rest and to think. Some came because they hoped to be cured of sickness. Some came because they wished to hear his stories and teachings about the new way of living.

Ezekias tied his donkey to an olive tree at the edge of the crowd and wriggled closer and closer to the Teacher. Being little might make it hard to see *over* crowds, but it did make it easy to squeeze *through* crowds.

Jesus' teaching was very different from what Ezekias usually heard. When the rabbi spoke in the synagogue, Ezekias always let his mind wander where it would. This Teacher was talking about things that Ezekias could understand, things that were important enough to hold the attention of the grownups and yet so simple that every word was plain to Ezekias. He was talking about everyday things like being friendly with neighbors, helping people, sharing everything, putting other people's happiness first. Ezekias had heard other people talk about being helpful, but no one had ever made him feel, as the Teacher did, that thinking of others' comfort was the happiest way of living. There was something about Jesus' face that showed he had found his own happiness in helping others. Ezekias began to wish there was something kind he could do for someone right then and there.

Jesus stopped speaking, looked at the position of the sun and then at the crowds of people.

"Philip," he turned to one of his closest friends. "How are we to buy bread, so that these people may eat?"

Philip looked puzzled. He rapidly reckoned there must be five thousand people, and he realized that five thousand can eat a great deal of food.

"Two hundred denarii would not buy enough bread for each of them to get a little," said Philip.

It was then that Ezekias remembered the lunch which his

mother had fixed for him. Shyly he touched the sleeve of Andrew, a close friend of Jesus.

"This is not much." Ezekias untied the corners of the cloth which held his lunch and showed it to Andrew. "Just five barley loaves and two small fishes. I want to share it."

Andrew looked at the little flat, round loaves and the two small, cooked fish. It was a good lunch for one boy, but it seemed foolish to bother Jesus with it when he had the big problem of food for five thousand people on his mind. Then Andrew noticed the eagerness in Ezekias' face. Smiling, he thanked the boy and led him to Jesus.

"There is a lad here who has five barley loaves and two fish." Andrew felt almost ashamed that he had bothered Jesus with the boy's gift. He shrugged his shoulders and added, "But what are they among so many?"

Jesus' quick smile saved Ezekias from embarrassment. Taking the lunch in both hands, Jesus said to Andrew, Philip, and his other close friends, "Make the people sit down."

Ezekias looked at the multitude finding places to sit in groups on the grassy hillside. He looked at Jesus standing there, smiling and confident, holding the boy's lunch in his hand.

Then Ezekias watched proudly. We do not know just what happened. Some people believe that Jesus worked a miracle on the food, making it increase and increase until there was enough to feed five thousand people. Others believe that Jesus worked a miracle on men's hearts, putting in them the wish to share. Many of those in the crowd had probably planned to be away from home all day and had carried lunches. After hearing Jesus talk and after seeing one boy so eager to share his lunch, many must have felt the wish to share. When they started to share, others followed; because kindness is one of the most contagious things in the world.

There was a new song in Ezekias' heart as he untied the

little gray donkey to start on his journey homeward. He spied a group of weary, dusty children.

"Would you like to ride on my donkey?" It was a new Ezekias speaking. "The two smallest ones can ride. I will lead the donkey very carefully, and we can all go down together."

See John 6:1-14.

THE FIRST NEW ENGLAND SABBATH

A hideous cry pierced the December darkness. It came from the low woods that edged the sandy beach where ten Pilgrims and six of the "Mayflower's" crew were camped. "Woath woach ha ha hach woach!" It threatened again. The men did not need the sentinel's call, "Arm! Arm!" to waken them. Stiff from cold and from their scouting through the woods, sand, and beach in search of a place to settle, they staggered to their feet. They groped for muskets. Two men lighted gunpowder. Their shots cracked through the night. Then there was silence.

The men threw more of their hard-collected dry wood on the fire. In the brighter blaze they wondered together about the cry. They were brave men all, else they would not have volunteered to leave the safety of the "Mayflower," riding in the harbor and sheltered by the tip of Cape Cod. You have heard their names—Captain Miles Standish, John Carver, William Bradford, Edward Winslow, and others. Courageous as they were, they did wish they knew whether the cry was that of wild animals or of the Indians whose footprints they had seen that day.

"It's wolves or it's foxes," said one of the sailors. "I heard such a cry in Newfoundland."

The men lay down again behind the barricade, but their sleep was not so sound. Halfway between dreaming and waking, they had time to remember about the two months since they set sail from Plymouth, England. Tossing in the "Mayflower." Sighting land. Meeting solemnly in the "Mayflower" cabin to sign their compact. Putting together their small boat, called a "shallop," to carry scouting expeditions ashore. Exploring the sands and woods of Cape Cod. Finding clams, fish, springs of fresh water, abandoned Indian houses, fields where Indians had raised corn, mounds where Indians stored corn and beans. Spending their Sundays on the "Mayflower" in their accustomed way—resting and worshiping God. They had much to remember as they slept on the beach.

By five o'clock of this dark December morning they were awake and ready to start a new day. Some tried their muskets to see if they would go off. They aimed out to sea, but the sound cracked through the wooded land that rose behind them in the half-light of morning. They gathered for prayer, asking God to guide them as they tried to find the site for the new Pilgrim village. They were ready to eat breakfast when suddenly—

"Woath woach ha ha hach woach!" It was the same hideous cry that had pierced their sleep in the night. It seemed to come from many voices. Was it wolves, as the sailor had said, or foxes?

Then one of the men who had wandered from the barricade came running back. "They are men," he shouted. "Indians! Indians!" Arrows began to fly. The Pilgrims' muskets answered.

To this day that beach, on the inner side of the elbow of Cape Cod, is called "First Encounter Beach" after that skirmish. As the Pilgrims learned later, the Nauset Indians had suffered bad treatment from an English sea captain who captured twenty of their tribe to sell as slaves in England. These Indians did not know the difference between marauding white men and the Pilgrims, who had come to the new land with such different ideas—"the desire of carrying the Gospell of Christ into those forraigne parts, amongst those people that as yet have no knowledge, nor tast of God, as also to procure unto themselves and others a quiet and comfortable habytation." So the battle on the beach raged—arrows against gunpowder, with trees and barricades as forts. At last the Indians slipped back into the woods.

"So," wrote the Pilgrims in their journal, "after wee had given God thankes for our deliverance, wee tooke our shallop and went our journay." But their troubles had only begun, as the next entry in their journal tells:

After we had sayled an houre or two, it began to snow and raine, and to be bad weather; about the midst of the afternoone, the winde increased and the Seas began to be very rough, and the hinges of the rudder broke, so that we could steere no longer with it, but two men with much adoe were faine to serve with a couple of Oares; the Seas were growne so great, that we were much troubled and in great danger, and night grew on: Anon Master Coppin bad us be of good cheere, he saw the Harbour; as we drew neare, the gale being stiffe, and we bearing great sayle to get in, split our Mast in 3 peices, and were like to have cast away our Shallop, yet by Gods mercy recovering our selves, wee had the floud with us, and struck into the Harbour.

In the harbor they found an island with a sandy beach where they were able to run their small boat ashore. Not knowing when they might hear another cry and feel another shower of arrows, they slept on the island that night. The next day, Saturday, they spent exploring the island and building a barricade to use as their camp. Within sight lay the mainland, more friendly and fertile in appearance than the sands and scrubby woodlands of Cape Cod. They were eager to get across to the land and see if this might be a good place to build their new Pilgrim village. They were eager to get back to the "Mayflower" and report to their friends. Time was precious, as winter snows were beginning to fall. They must build some sort of shelter for their families before the dead of winter. Every day counted.

The story so far, and much more, comes from entries dated December 6, 7, 8, and 9, in the Pilgrims' journal. We would expect the entry for December 10 to tell of their trip to explore the mainland. But the entry for that day has just six words.

The Pilgrims, unlike some of us today, believed in keeping *all* of God's commandments. They did not pick and choose the ones it would be pleasant and convenient to obey. So, even when looking across at the mainland which they were so eager to explore, they remembered God's commandment: "Remember the sabbath day, to keep it holy. Six days you shall labor, and do all your work; but the seventh day is a sabbath to the Lord your God; in it you shall not do any work." Do you suppose they told God, "You know how we rested and worshiped and kept the sabbath holy on the 'Mayflower.' We'll begin again as soon as we have found a place to settle. But with winter coming on, and all, we can't give you a day right now."

The six words written on that first day that our Pilgrim Fathers spent ashore in the new land were: *"On the Sabboth day wee rested."* And we can be sure that they prayed as they rested, thanking God for his protection and asking him to make them brave and wise as they continued their search for the place to build the new colony where there would be freedom to worship him.

All facts and quotations are from *Relation or Journall of the beginning and proceedings of the English Plantation at Plimoth,* better known as *Mourt's Relation.*

SLINGSHOTS AND CHURCH BELLS

Seventy years ago in the springtime two seven-year-old boys who lived across the seas in Alsace found some forked sticks, some rubber, and some scraps of leather. These small boys—their names were Henry Bräsch and Albert Schweitzer —did just what any boys might do if they had forked sticks, rubber, and scraps of leather at the same time. Each made a slingshot. For a while the two boys had plenty of fun shooting pebbles at targets. But Henry began to want something more exciting to do.

"Let's have more fun," he said to Albert. "Let's go into the woods and shoot at birds."

Shooting birds was not at all Albert Schweitzer's idea of fun. Even when he was too young to go to school, the boy had a special love for all living creatures. He used to wonder why the evening prayers were all about human beings—never about animals.

After his mother had prayed with him and had kissed him good night, Albert used to say a special little prayer of his own: "O heavenly Father, protect and bless all things that have breath; guard them from all evil, and let them sleep in peace." He would never have had Henry's idea of using the slingshots on birds.

"Come on, Albert!" Henry started toward the woods. And Albert followed. Shooting birds seemed horrible to him, but letting Henry think he was a sissy seemed even worse. Albert Schweitzer was only seven years old. He had not yet learned that it did not really hurt when people laughed at him. He was a quiet, rather shy boy. He hated to seem queer or different.

And so Albert followed, wishing all the time that he had the courage to say: "No!" The boys reached the woods. It was early springtime, the week before Easter. The birds were singing merrily in trees that were just in bud. There was no place for the birds to hide, if they had known there was any reason to hide. When Albert heard the beautiful morning songs of the birds, he felt even worse about what he must do.

Henry crouched down and fitted a stone to the leather of his sling. He nodded to Albert to do the same, and Albert obeyed him. Henry took careful aim and looked over to see if Albert was aiming too. Albert aimed. He told himself that he must shoot as soon as Henry did. He could not face being called a sissy.

Henry pulled the elastic, just ready to let the stone fly toward the bird that was singing his song of springtime and morning. At that very minute the church bells of the village began to ring, calling people to worship in the services of Holy Week. Henry did not think much of the bells, but to Albert the ringing "was a voice from heaven." He dropped his slingshot, jumped up from his crouching position, shouted, and waved his arms around to shoo the birds away. The birds took wing. They were safe from Henry's slingshot. Then, without a word, Albert turned and ran home as fast as a seven-year-old boy can run.

Years afterward, when Albert Schweitzer had become one of the best-loved missionary doctors our world has ever known, he told the story of the slingshots and the church bells. He added: "Ever since then, when the Passiontide bells ring out to the leafless trees and the sunshine, I reflect with a rush of grateful emotion how on that day their music drove deep into my heart the commandment: 'Thou shalt not kill.'"

You have perhaps heard of Albert Schweitzer and of his great work as a missionary doctor in Africa. You may have heard that he is famous for his skill as a surgeon, for his playing of the organ, for his books about the Christian religion, and for his great love that includes all human beings and all living creatures as well.

Since the day the church bells gave him courage to do what he himself thought was right, he has helped God to make the prayer of his childhood come true: "O heavenly Father, protect and bless all things that have breath; guard them from all evil, and let them sleep in peace."

This incident is reported by Albert Schweitzer in his book *Memoirs of Childhood and Youth*. Copyright 1949 by The Macmillan Company. Quotations are by permission of The Macmillan Company and George Allen & Unwin Ltd.

THE HOUSE THAT PRAYER BUILT

When she was only five years old, Mary knew that she wanted to be a doctor. What is more, she knew that she must work in a place where there were not enough doctors to take care of all the sick people. She knew because she had heard missionaries from Siam telling how much more they could have helped if they had been doctors. Now, many years later, Mary Sloop remembers her five-year-old self promising God that she would be a medical missionary when she grew up.

When Mary grew up, she kept her promise to become a doctor, even though in those days a girl studying medicine was thought to be a queer person. She tried to keep her promise to go to Siam. She had spent so many years, however, taking care of her sick mother that the mission board decided she was too old to go to a new and difficult country. But she knew there were plenty of places in America where there was much sickness and where there were no doctors within call.

She married Dr. Eustace Sloop, who felt as she did about helping the people who needed them most. In 1911 they settled in a lonely mountain community in North Carolina, and Crossnore has become a very different community because the Sloops have been there. The two doctors found that their mountain friends needed something in addition to medicine and operations, important as those were. The people who lived in little log houses in the hills about Crossnore needed a church, schools, craft industries, better homes, better roads, and better farming methods.

As Mrs. Sloop went about helping her people, she never forgot what she had known so well when she was only five years old. She remembered to talk over her plans and her problems with God. She did not sit back and wait for God to perform miracles for her. She worked and prayed till she had done everything within her power. Then as she kept on praying, she trusted God to do the part that she and her mountain friends could not do. Her life is full of stories about answers to prayers that were backed by work and faith.

Here is just one example of these stories.

The "donkey barn" was too small for the twenty-two boys who had to sleep there when they moved in from their homes high in the hills to go to school at Crossnore. It was really a dormitory but was nicknamed the "donkey barn" because it looked more like a shed for animals than a house for boys six to twelve years old. The boys slept on double-decker beds left over from World War I. Two or three boys could crowd into a bed built for one doughboy—three on the bottom deck and two on the upper. There was not enough space around the double-deckers to store their few clothes, to say nothing of their treasures. There was not any of the elbow room that any boy six to twelve years old needs so badly. There was no space for other boys who wanted to come to school.

The boys talked often about a new dormitory. Mrs. Sloop talked with them. She wrote to friends who were interested in the school at Crossnore. And, of course, she talked with God about the boys' needing a better home than the "donkey barn." The bigger boys of the carpentry class could do much of the work, but materials cost such a lot of money that was not there.

One afternoon in spring one of the smaller boys was feeling that they would be sleeping in the "donkey barn" forever. "Mis' Sloop," he said, "we ain't never agoin' to get our new dormitory."

"Oh, yes, we are!" Mrs. Sloop was just as tired of waiting as he was. "And we're going to begin work on it right now. You tell the other boys to get tools for chopping and digging. Then you all come to the hillside where the new dormitory is going to be built. I'll meet you there."

Then for two hours those twenty-two boys, from the youngest to the oldest, worked as hard as any boys could work. First they cut off the underbrush that sprawled all over the hillside. Then they dug up any roots that were small enough for them to handle. And as they worked, they talked together about the new dormitory that would some day rise on that spot.

Ding dong. It was the first supper bell. It was time for the boys to put up their tools and wash for supper. But Mrs. Sloop remembered her lifelong habit of talking things over with God.

"Wait a minute," she told the boys. "Let's all put down our tools now and stand in a ring. And we're all going to say a prayer and ask God to give us the money for this dormitory as soon as he thinks it's best for us to have it. And also we'll ask him to teach us to be worthy of a new dormitory, to behave so well that people will want us to have a dormitory. And we'll get the money."

Then as the sunset made the sky red behind the hills, the boys bowed their heads and talked with God. One after another around the circle the twenty-two boys spoke twenty-two prayers. They asked God to help them deserve a new dormitory. They promised God they would study hard and behave themselves. They told God they would work with him to build the dormitory. The last supper bell was ringing as they opened their eyes.

A little boy from one of the drabbest homes on all the mountainside stepped up to Mrs. Sloop. He was pulling something out of his pants pocket.

"Here's you some money to start on." He put a penny in her hand.

The boys had done what they could. Now they and Mrs. Sloop could only have faith that God would hear their prayer. The months went on. The boys did their best to live up to their promises to God. Mrs. Sloop did her best to let people know that there were twenty-two schoolboys who deserved a better home than the "donkey barn."

Then the answer to their prayer came. It was a letter carrying a check large enough to build and furnish a dormitory to hold many more than the twenty-two boys. And it was labeled, "For the boys' dormitory."

The fine new building that was built could never be nicknamed a "donkey barn," but it could be nicknamed "the house that prayer built"—prayer mixed with large quantities of work and faith.

Adapted from the book *Miracle in the Hills* by Dr. Mary T. Martin Sloop with Legette Blythe. Copyright, 1953, and published by the McGraw-Hill Book Company, Inc., N. Y. C.

THE SHEPHERD AND THE WALLET

The agricultural expert from the United States was more used to riding in a car than on the back of a small horse picking its way over a rough mountain trail in the Middle East. It was a long hot trip to the tribal village from the car parked on the dusty highway. As he jogged along in the caravan of pack animals and riders, the American was remembering what friends had said when they heard he was going to this mountain village to try to help the tribesmen improve their livestock.

"You are letting yourself in for a tough time, Steve," friends had told him. "The tribesmen of that village have a low opinion of anyone from outside, and of foreigners in particular. They won't listen to your advice about their sheep, goats, and cows. But they will take everything except your advice. Keep your stuff locked and hidden while you are there."

But Steve did not think long of his friends' warning. He was in the habit of going where his work called him without worrying about himself. He was in the habit of making friends instead of enemies, because he had Jesus' way of seeing the good in people and trusting them to bring out the best in themselves. When he was a boy, he had heard the stories of Jesus' finding four ordinary fishermen and making them his disciples, and of Jesus' inviting the hated taxgatherer Zacchaeus to come down from the sycamore tree and be his friend. He had found that Jesus' way of trusting folks worked. He did not stop to think much about it. Trusting and liking people was just his way of living. So he did not worry about tribesmen who hated all outsiders and foreigners in particular.

Steve and the men who traveled with him followed the trail on and on toward the mountain village. Finally he climbed down from the horse to rest himself by walking. Just then they came upon shepherds with their flocks. The American and his companions stopped to talk with the men about the animals. The newcomers were so friendly that the shepherds forgot they were strangers. One of them offered to go with the visitors to show them the easiest trail to the village. As they plodded along in the heat, the shepherd told the American he should be riding instead of walking.

"I like to walk," answered Steve. "You know I am a shepherd like you."

The tribesman laughed to hear the learned man from America call himself a shepherd. "You a shepherd like me?"

"When I was a little boy, I used to tend sheep and goats on the hilly pastures of Turkey," Steve assured him. "I know what it is to hear hungry jackals howling when I am alone with the flocks on the range."

The shepherd laughed again. Plainly he could not believe that his guest had ever tended sheep and goats in the hills. Steve knew that there was no point in telling the tribesman how he lost his parents in World War I, was rescued by a Near East Relief orphanage, was educated in American mission schools in Turkey and Greece, had gone to the United States to study animal husbandry, had become an American citizen, and now had come back to the Middle East to help farmers improve their livestock.

Though the tribesman laughed at Steve's calling himself a shepherd, he liked him for it. "Let me carry your jacket," he offered.

"Oh, I can carry it without any trouble," answered Steve.

"You do not trust me to carry it," said the shepherd. "You think I will steal the money from your pocket."

"Not at all!" The American took his wallet from his jacket pocket and handed it to the shepherd. "I will carry the coat, and you will carry the money for me."

The tribesman opened the wallet and looked inside at a roll of paper money larger than he had ever had in his hands before.

71

Probably it was more money than he had ever seen at one time. He folded the wallet and went rapidly up the trail. Used to that barren mountainside, he walked much faster than the others. Soon he disappeared behind a jagged hilltop. When the American and his friends reached that height, they saw the trail stretching empty ahead of them, upward till it wound out of sight around a hill.

"Do you ever expect to see that wallet again?" one of the men asked Steve.

"It never hurts a man to show him that you like him and trust him," was the answer. Even though shepherd and money had disappeared, the American was still living by Jesus' way of making men better by trusting them to be their best selves. Then they followed the rough trail upward to the village. They knew that the tribesmen would be polite to them, because people of the East are always polite to guests. They did not know, however, whether the tribesmen would be glad to see them or would listen to them.

But as soon as they were near the village, they found they had no reason to worry. The headman of the tribe came out, smiling, to greet them as though they were old friends. As they passed through the streets, they saw friendly smiles on every face. Children ran after them and called, "They have come! They have come!"

When the travelers reached the little square in the center of the village, they knew why they had been getting such a royal welcome from tribesmen who usually were suspicious of strangers. There was the shepherd of the hillside. He was showing the wallet to all his neighbors. He was opening it so that everyone could see the big roll of bills. He was telling in the proudest of voices about the foreigner who trusted him to carry his wallet.

"There he is!" The shepherd pointed at the American. "He asked me to carry his money. He trusted me!" Then he handed the wallet back to its owner. Steve put it in his pocket without even opening it to count the money. The villagers all smiled and nodded when they saw that he really did trust one of their own tribe, trusted him enough that he pocketed the wallet without counting to see if the money was all there.

In the days that followed, the tribesmen listened carefully to advice about their flocks. Whatever the American and his companions suggested, they agreed would be worth a good try. They were glad to take advice from a friend who had Jesus' way of liking people and trusting them to live at their best.

This is an experience of Dr. C. S. Stephanides, an agriculturist of the Foreign Operations Administration in Iran. He was the young hero of "The Constant Star" in my book *Stories for Junior Worship*.

BOYS AND GIRLS TODAY

A QUESTION FROM THE FBI

"I never saw that car before," said Jennifer, who was deep in a game of detectives with the neighborhood gang. The children all looked across the street at the car that had stopped in Jennifer's driveway. "And I never saw that man who is walking up to our door. I'll be back after I see who he is." As Jennifer started to cross the street toward home, she was still in the mood of the detective game. "I'll yell if I need help," she called back to her friends.

She stood behind the stranger as her mother opened the door.

"Mrs. Walker?" he asked.

"Yes, I am Mrs. Walker," answered Jennifer's mother.

"I am Mr. Stewart from the Federal Bureau of Investigation of the United States Department of Justice," he introduced himself.

"You mean the FBI?" Mrs. Walker's voice was nearly as surprised as Jennifer's own round eyes. "Please come in."

As the door closed behind Mr. Stewart, Jennifer dashed back across the street to report to her friends. After telling them what she had overheard, she said: "You listen outside our living-room window. The one toward the garden is open. I'll go in the house. I'll signal if we need help."

Of course, the children did not really expect that anything dangerous was going to happen in the Walker's house, but having a real live FBI man there was something that fitted into their game. They tiptoed across the street. The neighborhood children squatted silently under the window of the Walker's living room, while Jennifer went inside and sat on the floor beside her mother. The stranger was just finishing polite apologies for disturbing Mrs. Walker on a busy morning. The children had missed nothing worth hearing. Then the conversation went something like this.

"You have a neighbor named Mr. Henry Prentiss?" asked the FBI man.

"Oh, yes, a good friend of ours. The family lives next door," answered Mrs. Walker. Under the window the young detectives breathed heavily, especially Junior Prentiss.

"Mr. Prentiss is being considered by the State Department for a position in a country in the Middle East. I have been sent to this town to learn all I can about him and his family. You know it is terribly important that the people who represent the United States overseas should be the right sort in every way." Under the open window all eyes stared at Junior Prentiss.

"Oh, the State Department could make no mistake in sending Mr. Prentiss," the children heard Mrs. Walker say. Then followed question after question about Junior's father and family. The FBI man wanted to know all sorts of things. What clubs did Mr. Prentiss belong to? What were his wife's interests? Were the children well-behaved? Did the family go to church? Did they get on well with their neighbors? Were they completely loyal to the United States government? Could they keep a secret? On and on went the questions. Mrs. Walker answered them easily. Junior, under the window, grew prouder by the minute.

Then came the question: "What about their drinking habits? Does Mr. or Mrs. Prentiss use alcoholic drinks?"

"I have never known of their drinking alcohol in any form," answered Mrs. Walker. "Of course, I can't be sure that they never do, but I am certain that they do not have the habit of drinking. Is that important?"

"It's terribly important," answered the man from the FBI. "Anyone representing our country away from home has to be always on his best behavior and has to have a clear mind. The smartest man can make mistakes when he has been drinking.

A person who is usually polite might say something insulting. A person who is usually careful might say a careless thing. He might give away secret information after a drink or two had loosened his tongue. And, of course, if a person drinks a little, he may once in a while take more than he should. I do wish you were absolutely sure about their drinking habits."

"I know about them," spoke up Jennifer. The man from the FBI noticed her for the first time. The young detectives pressed closer below the open window to hear her. "You know how kids go to lots of refrigerators when they come home from school hungry. Well, in some of my friends' refrigerators there are cans or bottles that we must never touch. But in the Prentiss' refrigerator there's nothing but the sort of things any kid can drink—milk, fruit juice, soda, and that sort of stuff."

"Thanks," said the man from the FBI. "That's a good answer."

After Mr. Stewart had gone, the neighborhood children discussed his visit. "It really wasn't very exciting," Jennifer said. "We didn't learn much about how to be detectives, did we?"

"I learned a lot about something else," said Junior Prentiss, who was more sure than ever that he wanted to be just like his dad. "I learned that if you want to grow up to be the sort of person that can be trusted *always* to do the right thing, you better be careful what you drink. It pays to stick to milk and fruit juice and the drinks that are good for kids—no matter how old you get to be."

And the other boys and girls agreed that they had learned something very important, after all.

This story was suggested by an editorial in the New York *Herald Tribune*.

DON'T BE A MACKEREL

"Don't be a mackerel, Jan!" came the warning shout of her brother Walter.

Janet stopped so suddenly that she was knocked flat by the children racing after her toward the Bickford's orchard. Those who were ahead of her ran on to crawl through the barbed-wire fence, laugh at the "No Trespassing" sign, and climb into the trees that hung heavy with ripe red apples.

"What's the matter?" Adrian untangled herself from the jumble of arms and legs caused by Janet's sudden stop. "The Bickfords are all away—their dog, too. We saw them drive off in their car."

"All the kids are going!" urged Everett. "What's all this silly talk about mackerel? Ever since you came back from vacation, you two have been spoiling your own fun by telling each other, 'Don't be a mackerel!' "

"Yeah," agreed Stella. "Those crazy fish keep you from doing what the rest of the gang does. And they make you do things we don't do."

"Of course, you're usually right," admitted Edgar. "But so what? What do mackerel have to do with it?"

"Do you really want to know?" asked Walter.

"You won't like it," warned Janet.

"Sure. Tell us," said Everett. "We can take it."

"We always used to do whatever the gang did. You know that," said Walter. "Whether it was good or bad, we'd follow along just so we wouldn't be different from the rest of you."

The children nodded. They knew that Janet and Walter used to be as quick as any of them to talk themselves out of any sort of trouble with the old all-the-kids-are-doing-it excuse.

For the moment they forgot their friends in the apple trees and gathered around Janet and Walter to hear their story.

"When we were at Cape Cod this summer, we made friends with a fisherman named Mr. Elwood," began Walter. "He owned the fishweirs that were straight out from the beach where we played."

"What do you mean—fishweirs?" interrupted Adrian.

"They're nets nailed to tall poles that are driven deep into the sand under the water," explained Walter. "They are set like fences, so that it is easy for the fish to get in but hard for them to get out. At high tide there is enough water in the weirs for the fish to swim, but it's shallow enough that the fishermen in hip boots can wade among them with their scooping nets."

Then Janet took up the story of their fisherman friend. "Mr. Elwood used to go out to his weirs every day at low tide. He would drive over the sand flats in his pickup truck. Sometimes we would ride out with him, and sometimes we would start earlier and walk out so we'd be there when he came. He let us wade inside the weirs with him. It was there that we saw the green mackerel swimming round and round in a bunch—a "school of mackerel," the fishermen called it. Because they were all following each other, they never saw the easy way out into the open sea again."

"How did they get inside?" asked Everett.

"There were rows of pine branches driven into the sand leading up to the entrance of the nets on either side," Walter explained. "They were practically covered at high tide but made a sort of fence under the water. Whichever direction the fish were swimming, they would bump into one of these rows of brush. If each fish had done its own exploring, it could have found its way through the branches. But they were traveling in a gang. The first ones took the easy way and turned aside. Then all the ones that followed did the same. When they turned, they swam directly through the opening of the outer circle of the big net. If they had used their brains, if any, they could have found their way out the same way they came in.

81

But fish that swim in schools don't do their own thinking. They just follow. And so they swam round and round in circles, staying close together and never finding the way out. And at low tide there they were, swimming in circles, ready for Mr. Elwood to scoop with his hand-nets as many as he needed to take to market that day. There were other fish caught in the weirs, too; but at the time of year we were there, more mackerel than anything else, because they were swimming in the biggest schools."

"Caught because they followed the gang," said Adrian, who was getting the point. "Caught because they said in fish language, 'All the crowd is doing it!'"

Then Edgar put a hand on either side of his mouth and yelled in a voice that carried beyond the barbed-wire fence and the "No Trespassing" signs to the children in the apple trees, "Hey, kids! Get out of those trees! Don't be mackerel!"

THE BATTLE OF THE BIRTHDAYS

The bus labeled "School District Number 1" stopped beside the mailbox of the Bartlett farm. Beth Bartlett climbed on the bus and swished down the aisle. That this was a special day for Beth showed in the tilt of her red-scarved head, in the swing of her golden-brown pigtails, in the excited shine of her wide blue eyes, and in the pride with which she carried a package of pink envelopes.

At the same time, on the opposite side of Spring Glen, the bus labeled "School District Number 2" stopped beside the tree-lined driveway of the Aldrich farm. Children nudged each other as Alan Aldrich jostled down the aisle of that school bus. That this was a special day for Alan showed in the saucy angle of his cap, in the friendly punches he gave his best pals, in the triumphant gleam of his dancing brown eyes, and in the way he pretended not to be conscious of the thick bunches of white envelopes sticking out of both overcoat pockets.

When the buses reached the schoolyard, most of the children stopped for a snowball fight. Beth and Alan went straight to Miss Webb's room, Grade Six. Beth began at one end of the room putting a pink envelope on each desk but her own. Alan began at the other end of the room putting a white envelope on each desk but his own. Each child pretended not to know what the other was doing.

Other children began coming through the door. They all pounced upon their two envelopes and tore them open. The boys opened their white envelopes first and tried not to look interested when they opened their pink ones. The girls looked into their pink envelopes first but could not hide their curiosity when they peeked into the white ones. No one was more curious about the pink envelope than Alan, and no one was more curious about the white envelope than Beth. Each knew that inside those envelopes lay the clues to the winner in this year's battle of the birthdays.

"It is too bad that Beth and Alan had to be born on the same day," Miss Webb thought as she opened her envelopes. "Spring Glen hospital would have rocked on January 16 if it could have looked ahead and seen the yearly battles that would be fought."

This is what was in the white envelopes: "See Martin the Magician at the Aldrich Farm, Bundy Road, 4 P.M., Tuesday, January 16. Sleight of hand. Juggling. Refreshments."

And this is what was on the pink invitations: "Red and Silver, the Bartlett horses, will take you for a sleigh ride on Tuesday, January 16. Be at the Bartlett Farm on the Town Line Road at 4 P.M. Birthday cake after the ride."

The battle of the birthdays was on. It raged all that week as the sixth grade discussed the relative excitements of a sleigh ride and a magician who could also juggle.

"Red and Silver are wonderful horses," someone would say. "Most of the farmers around here have nothing left but tractors."

"I never saw Martin the Magician," another would say. "But we've heard Alan brag plenty about his Uncle Martin who worked his way through college by giving juggling and magic shows."

Most years it was fairly easy to choose. Beth's party would sound sort of girlish, while Alan's would sound fit for boys. But this year it was different. The boys did not want to miss the sleigh ride, and the girls did not want to miss the magician.

By Saturday, Beth and Alan were not speaking to each other. On Sunday when they met at church school, they sat as far apart as possible.

At first their Sunday-school teacher found it hard to interest the class in the study of I Cor. 13, Paul's chapter about Christian love. But soon she had the class playing charades. Some of them acted out different verses or phrases of the chapter, while the rest studied their Bibles to guess which verse was being represented. Even Beth and Alan joined in the guessing.

Carlton chose a team to act out the phrase "If I give away all I have." Mary's team acted the seventh verse, "Love bears all things. . . ."

Peter's team, looking mischievous, acted a quarrel over which of two birthday parties would be the better. A boy and a girl played the parts of two disagreeable children, each bragging about his own party.

"My Aunt Hannah will be at *my* party," said the boy. "She eats fire and swallows swords and throws knives and walks on the ceiling."

"At *my* party we are going to have two teams of trained Huskies straight from Alaska," said the girl. "These Eskimo dogs will race over the snow while we take turns driving."

Beth's face grew red. Alan squirmed till his chair creaked. The teacher saw that something was wrong, but she had no idea what it could be. The guesses came thick and fast from children whose eyes were skimming over the verses of I Cor. 13.

"Love is not jealous," guessed Ruth.

"Love is not boastful," guessed Mary.

"Love does not insist on its own way," guessed Carlton.

"It could be any of those," said Peter, as he and his team sat down again. "We meant it for 'Love is not jealous,' but the others fit, too."

"I see one trouble," said the teacher. "You acted what love is *not*. Your charade showed what happens when there is no love. If Paul had been writing about what you acted, he would have written something like this: 'Where there is no love, there is jealousy. Those who do not love are boastful. Those who do not love insist on their own way.' How about playing those verses the way Paul wrote them, instead of in reverse?"

"I see what you mean." Peter beckoned his team into a corner to plan a new playing.

Beth's hand went up timidly. "May I choose a team to act the same scene? I need just one to play it with me. I choose Alan."

"Me?" Alan stared at her in surprise.

"Yes, you!" Beth was herself again now that she had made the plunge. She led the way to a corner of the room. Dragging his feet to show his disapproval, Alan followed her.

There was a buzzing of whispers in the two corners as Peter's and Beth's teams planned how to act out a solution to the battle of the birthdays in a way that would fit Paul's great chapter on Christian love. The children who remained in their seats were watching Beth and Alan. Peter's team, ready to perform, had been in their seats several minutes before Beth and Alan finally joined them.

Just then there was organ music from the church sanctuary. The teacher looked at her wrist watch. "Oh, how fast the time has gone. Time for church now. Shall we continue next Sunday?"

"Next Sunday will be too late," Beth announced.

"Beth, we can act it out during the week," suggested Alan.

"And the rest of you can guess when it happens," said Beth.

The next morning the bus labeled "School District Number 1" stopped beside the mailbox of the Bartlett farm. There was a hush in the morning chatter as Beth, scattering smiles to right and to left, walked down the aisle. That this was a happy day for Beth showed in the upward curves of her pretty mouth and in the gay way she swung a package of pink envelopes.

At the same time, on the opposite side of Spring Glen, the bus labeled "School District Number 2" stopped at the Aldrich farm. Alan whistled as he climbed into the school bus. That this was a happy day for Alan showed in the twinkle of his brown eyes and in the jaunty way he was stuffing white cards into his pockets.

When the buses reached the schoolyard, all of the sixth

graders hurried to their room. They knew something was in the air. Most of them were sitting in their own seats when Beth passed out pink envelopes to the first rows and Alan passed white cards to the last rows.

It really was not necessary for them to give out all the invitations because the first children to receive them were reading aloud. Soon everyone in the room knew that the message in the pink envelopes and on the white cards was one and the same, even though some were written in Beth's round hand and some were typed with only a few mistakes on the Aldrich's typewriter.

This is what the sixth grade read: "Meet at the Bartlett Farm, Town Line Road, 3:30 P.M. tomorrow. Sleigh ride to the Aldrich Farm, Bundy Road, to see Martin the Magician. Sleigh ride back to the Bartlett Farm. Two birthday cakes with ice cream."

During the cheering Peter walked to Miss Webb's desk and whispered to her. He took the Bible from between the book ends on her desk and hunted through the pages. He soon found what he wanted.

"Beth and Alan have just played the charade they did not have time to finish in church school yesterday," said Peter. "I have found the verses they were acting.

" 'Love is not jealous or boastful; it is not arrogant or rude. Love does not insist on its own way.' "

Then Beth's hand shot up. "Peter made one mistake. Alan and I aren't acting the verses," said Beth. "We're *living* them."

ANITA'S HOMEWORK

This story took place in Mexico. It might have happened just as easily in any state north of the Rio Grande.

Anita was lazy about her schoolwork, especially about her homework. There were so many things to do after school that were more fun than arithmetic or geography! Nevertheless, every afternoon the teacher assigned homework, and every morning she expected a neat page of answers from each boy and each girl.

Anita's friend Carmen liked to do homework. She took pride in the correct and tidy papers that she brought to school each morning. This habit of Carmen's gave Anita an idea.

"Would you like to earn five pesetas each school day?" Anita asked Carmen.

"Of course!" answered Carmen. "How can I?"

"I'll pay you five pesetas every day if you'll let me copy your homework." Anita saw a doubtful look on Carmen's face, so added a teasing, "Please—to make me happy. You know how I hate doing homework."

"It would not be honest," objected Carmen. Then Anita begged and teased till Carmen felt she would lose her friend if she refused.

The lazy Anita thought she had made a fine bargain. In just a few minutes before school each morning she could copy Carmen's careful work. She never had to think. She never had to figure or look up answers in books. What was five pesetas to pay for a whole afternoon of fun or idling? Some of the children knew about the copied homework, but they did not tell. The teacher did not know.

The only trouble, so far as Anita could see, was that Carmen sat too far away to be of any help during class. When the teacher asked her a question, Anita was on her own. When there was a written test, there was no paper near enough to copy—except that of Domingo, who made mistakes. The longer Anita carried on her bargain with Carmen, the worse her reciting and tests became. She felt the teacher looking at her in a strange way as she said, "Anita! Anita! Why is your classwork so poor when your homework is so good?"

By the time the teacher found out about the bargain, it was too late. Anita was so far behind the class that she had to repeat the grade when Carmen and her other friends were promoted.

She did stay in the same Sunday-school class, however, and enjoyed the favorite game with the others. The teacher would describe to the class a problem in everyday living. Then they would divide into small groups to hunt a Bible verse that solved the problem.

One day the question was, "Your friend wants to copy your homework and expects your help on examinations. What verse could you read to him from the Bible to support your refusal?" The question was not about whether it was right to help a friend cheat. Everyone knew the answer to that, because everyone knew what had happened to Anita when Carmen helped her cheat. The question was to find a Bible verse to explain why it was wrong.

The class divided into groups to think over all the Bible verses they knew that might possibly be the answer. But there was not a word in the Bible about homework. There was nothing they could find about geography or arithmetic. There were many verses telling why it is a sin to lie or steal or cheat. There were verses against laziness. But where was a verse that explained why it is wrong to make it easy for someone else to cheat and to be lazy?

At last one group found the answer. It was a verse they all knew. It is a verse you know also: "Whatever you wish that men would do to you, do so to them" (Matt. 7:12).

Some of the children had to have it explained to them why the familiar Golden Rule answered the problem. But not Anita! She was sure as sure can be that helping another person to cheat, no matter how hard that person teases, is not doing "whatever you wish that men would do to you."

Source: *Christian World Facts* (1954), p. 51, a publication of the Division of Foreign Missions of the National Council of the Churches of Christ in the U.S.A.

THE HALFWAY SAMARITAN

"Chu-ug—chu-ug—chu-ug" went the motor of the car as it sputtered and gave up.

"Out of gas?" Kirk asked his mother, who was driving.

"Out of gas," she agreed after checking the gauge. She was able to steer the car to the side of the road before it stopped rolling. Then Kirk and his mother sat side by side on the front seat and waited. "Lucky we are here on the main road," she said. "Some chance to be pushed. There's a gas station just beyond the railroad tracks, on the crossroads."

Mother opened the car door so that she could wave her S O S signals to passing motorists. A shining maroon car came purring along. Mother waved, and Kirk shouted, "Will you give us a push?" But the driver did not so much as turn his head.

A green roadster sped toward them. Kirk beckoned, and Mother called, "We need a push!" The driver saw them, seemed about to lessen his speed, then drove on.

"I feel like the man in the Bible story," said Kirk. "You know, the one that fell among thieves who left him by the side of the road half-dead."

"We're not exactly half-dead, but I see what you mean," she agreed. "That big maroon car was like the priest who passed by on the other side of the road. The green roadster was like the Levite who passed the wounded man without stopping. According to that, our luck ought to be changing and the next car should be driven by our good Samaritan."

And it was. At least the man started out to be a good Samaritan. He pulled his black sedan with its out-of-state license to a stop beside their car.

"In trouble?" he asked.

"We are out of gas," explained Kirk's mother.

"Would a push help?" asked the stranger.

"There's a gas station about a quarter of a mile from here. It's on the first crossroad at our right. It's just beyond the railroad track," explained Mother. "If you would not mind pushing—"

But she did not need to finish her sentence. The man had already measured bumper heights with his eye and pulled in behind their car. Clank went his bumper on theirs. The stalled car shot forward. When it slowed down, there came a second tap—a third—a fourth—a fifth. Soon they were at the crossroads. Just as Mother had twisted her steering wheel to make the right-hand turn toward the gas station, they felt the biggest push yet on their bumper. Their car spurted ahead, then rolled slowly, then came to a dead stop—in the exact center of the railroad tracks.

"Woops!" Kirk looked nervously up and down the tracks. "I hope our good Samaritan hurries with that next push. I don't like sitting here."

What began as, "Neither do I," ended in a scream. The automatic red lights began to flash their warning that a train was coming. The gates lowered in front of their stalled car. Other gates lowered behind it. They were trapped without possibility of help.

"Jump, Kirk, jump!" screamed Mother. But he was already leaping to safety and shouting, "Jump, Mom, jump!"

After the northbound train had passed, Kirk and his mother stood staring at the shattered pile of rubble that used to be their car. Finally Kirk came out of his shock enough to ask, "Where's our good Samaritan now?" But the black sedan with its out-of-state license was nowhere in sight.

And that was the last time that Kirk called him the good Samaritan. He thought of a better way to describe him—"the halfway Samaritan." And when he told about their accident, he used to say, "You remember that the good Samaritan in

Jesus' parable followed through when he helped. He took the sick man to a place where he would be safe, and he paid for his care, and then he promised to stop by again to see if anything more was needed. I'm for that kind of help! I've had enough of the halfway Samaritans who stop helping too soon!"

Based on a news item in the Hartford *Courant*.

FAIR ARE THE MEADOWS

"What's the surprise, Miss Mary?" Eleven girls bounced up from their wooden benches so fast that the paper flowers on the piano rustled. "You promised to tell as soon as we finished our lesson!"

Miss Mary, who had grown up among quiet voices, clapped her hands over her ears. Sometimes she felt her head would crack from listening to voices that were used to shouting above street noises and above the sounds of crowded apartments.

"Three churches have invited you to visit for two weeks this summer," said Miss Mary. "You will go to their community vacation church school every morning and then play or go on trips in the afternoon. You will live in homes of the people that belong to the three churches."

"Is it the country?" asked Rosa.

"It is. Cows and hens. Flowers and birds. Grasshoppers and mountains. Meadows and woodlands."

"Ya-a-a-ay," squealed ten of the girls.

"Meadows and woodlands!" repeated Rita. Those words reminded her of a hymn they sometimes sang. She had never understood what it meant.

The girls chattered as they went into the street and dodged past children at play or grownups chatting in the spring sunshine. The girls turned in at different doorways that led up dark stairs to their apartments.

Rita stood a few minutes in front of her doorway. She had to get used to the idea of going to the country. She supposed it might be like Central Park—only bigger, with animals. She knew so little of what was beyond her own small world, bounded on the east by the endless traffic of buses and trucks on Second Avenue, and on the west by the noisy Third Avenue elevated train.

She knew about country things, especially cowboys, from the moving pictures she saw whenever there was enough money for a ticket. In school, too, she had learned about the world beyond East Harlem. And for the past few years young people like Miss Mary had been showing a different way of living.

Rita was too small to remember the first days of the East Harlem Protestant Parish, but her mother liked to tell her about the three young men who suddenly appeared and began to do friendly things for anyone who needed help. "They weren't satisfied just to get us to go to the churches they started in empty store fronts," Rita's mother would say. "They were always around playing with the kids and helping folks who were in any sort of trouble. They made us feel friendly toward neighbors we used to hate. They showed us that religion was more than just singing a hymn in church on Sundays."

Rita turned into the doorway and went up the three flights of narrow dark stairs that led to the apartment of three rooms that her family shared with her uncle and his four children. She did not notice how dark and crowded the rooms were, because she had never lived any other way.

From that day till the day when the car came from the country town, there was excitement for the girls of Miss Mary's class. When it was time to go, they had been ready for days, with their small cardboard suitcases packed.

Eleven girls loaded into the two cars—the one that had come from the country and Miss Mary's station wagon. Families were on the sidewalk to wave good-by. Heads popped out of windows all up and down the tall apartment houses. Eleven girls were shouting at once—to their families, to each other, to the heads in the windows, to Miss Mary, and to the children who had stopped their play to watch. The cars moved slowly down the street where games of ball or jump rope stopped to let them pass. They turned onto the avenue and headed north. Home was out of sight. New things were ahead. And not one of those new things did the girls meet in silence!

"The park! The park!" they shrieked when they left the city and turned onto a broad highway edged with lawns and trees.

"A cowboy town! A cowboy town!" they shouted as they saw their first small village, with houses clustered around a few stores, a church, and a school.

"Cows! Just like in the pictures!" they yelled as they passed a meadow with cows grazing beside a shining brook.

"Hens! Bigger than pigeons!" they shouted as they saw a yard full of plump Rhode Island Reds busily scratching for grain.

Every horse in a pasture, every pig rooting in an orchard, every cow waiting at a barnyard gate brought squeals from the girls. Every pond made them beg to stop and put on their new bathing suits. Every stretch of woodland made them wonder about wild animals. Every mountain brought "ohs" of surprise.

Before dark they were at their homes-for-two-weeks in the country town with its broad and shady lawns. In almost every home there was a child near their own age to greet them. Each house had trees, flowers, places to play, and so many rooms. And there were porches bigger than dozens of fire escapes put together.

The first night was not easy for Rita. It was strange to have a bed in a room by herself. Out-of-doors, instead of the familiar rumble of the Elevated and the cars on the avenues, there was a deathly quiet, except for a steady buzzing "chirrr-chirrr" under her window and a "twit-twit" farther away and higher up. There was another whistling, moaning sound that was altogether new to the ears of a child who had never slept near a tree before. But Rita was tired enough to go to sleep soon and wake up, wide-eyed, eager for what the new day would bring.

Every morning the eleven girls from East Harlem greeted each other and Miss Mary with whoops of joy when they met at the church. The soft voices of the town children, who had never needed to shout above street noises, seemed strange to the girls from the city. Soon the visitors found that they could make themselves heard without shouting. They found, too, that they were given things without having to fight for them. They learned that, if they kept still and listened, there were interesting stories about a man named Paul.

"He was sort of like the teachers and preachers at our church," said Julia, "leaving his home to tell people about Jesus."

Singing was what the girls liked best. Rita had a favorite song. She had sung it from the paper-covered hymnbooks in East Harlem, but the words had never meant anything to her:

> Fair are the meadows, fairer still the woodlands,
> Robed in the blooming garb of spring:
> Jesus is fairer, Jesus is purer,
> Who makes the woeful heart to sing.

In the afternoons the girls were out where they could see those meadows and those woodlands. At first they were afraid to walk through a trail that left the sidewalk or the road. Grasshoppers jumped at them. Bees and other insects buzzed about their heads. Hoptoads went leaping across the path. Who knew when a snake would come slithering out of the long grass? After they had walked a few trails, they stopped squealing at every grasshopper. They even made friends with a hoptoad, and all eleven of them loved him—until he gave up and had to have a funeral. They even climbed a small mountain, from whose top they looked down on what seemed to be toy villages with tiny midgets for people.

They loved the visits to farms. There was the farm where the baby lambs and mother sheep lined up on their side of the fence to baa at the girls, and the girls lined up on their side of the fence to baa back. There was the field of oats and the farmer who let them rub kernels of oats from their spikelets to see how the grain that later became oatmeal would taste. There was the barn full of cows where each girl had the chance to milk the gentlest one. In the pastures there were horses who would let themselves be petted by a row of girls at the gate. The words "Fair are the meadows" meant more and more to Rita.

There was the drive up the automobile road that led to the top of a mountain. Down and down they looked at houses small enough to belong to grasshoppers, at fenced meadows that looked like tiny pictures, at other mountains that spread on and on in tiers. They climbed up the lookout and used the telescope. They rode down the mountain road, first through piled rocks and then through woods. "Fairer still the woodlands" meant more and more to Rita.

Most exciting was the overnight trip to the Girl Scout cabin on Northwest Hill. They loved carrying packs and choosing bunks, cooking hot dogs on an open fire, games and fun songs after supper, the service of worship around the campfire. A thin chip of a new moon looked much nearer than in the city. The stars sparkled in a more friendly way over the tops of the trees than they used to do in the gap between rows of city houses. Between songs the girls each gave a "thank-you" prayer. Rita liked it best when they sang:

> Fair is the sunshine, fairer still the moonlight,
> And all the twinkling starry host:
> Jesus shines brighter, Jesus shines purer
> Than all the angels heaven can boast.

She knew that she would look up more often at the moonlight and the twinkling starry host, even when she was back among the tall rows of crowded houses of the city. There would be no meadows and no woodlands to see there, but the memory of them would be in her mind forever.

SEASONAL STORIES

THE PACKAGE FROM THE COUNTRY

EASTER

Carmen and Pedro were looking out the cracked window of their fourth-floor tenement when the mail truck stopped directly below them. The postman took a large parcel from the truck and started toward the door which the Nazario family shared with dozens of others.

"Could be for us!" Pedro headed for the stairs, just in case.

"Could be from the country!" Carmen was close behind him.

Since their two weeks as "fresh-air guests" in a country home a long train-ride away from their crowded section of the city, the postman seemed to have learned where they lived. There had been pencil boxes as school began in September, dates and nuts at Thanksgiving, toys at Christmas, red-heart candies for Valentine's Day. There had been letters from Priscilla and George, the two children on the farm where they had visited. Carmen and Pedro were thinking of all these surprises as they raced down the dark, narrow stairway—thinking and hoping.

"For us?" Pedro asked the postman who was studying the names in the dim hall.

"For Carmen and Pedro Nazario," read the postman.

It was hard waiting to open the package till they had climbed the three long flights of stairs. They took turns carrying, the better to guess what the new surprise might be.

"Box awful big," said Carmen while Pedro was carrying it.

"But light," said Pedro. "Big to weigh so little."

At last the children were in their own two rooms. They

103

were alone, because their mother was a waitress in a restaurant. They cut the string that tied the package, tore off the brown wrapping paper, and bumped heads over the box as Carmen lifted the cover. Pedro snatched away the green waxed paper that covered their gift. Then they groaned in disappointment.

"Dry sticks!" Pedro wanted to cry.

"What they good for?" Carmen wanted to cry—and she did.

"Letter was fastened outside." Pedro fumbled through the pile of torn wrapping paper on the floor. "Might tell what they good for."

It was Carmen, who always got "A" in reading, who opened the letter

Dear Carmen and Pedro,
Put these branches in a jar of water. You will have a surprise by Easter.
Your friends,
Priscilla and George

There was no vase in the Nazarios' two rooms. People who live where there are no fields or gardens have no need of vases unless there is extra money for buying flowers. There was never any extra money in the Nazario home. Pedro found an empty pickle jar that held half the twigs. Carmen put water in an empty milk bottle for the other half.

"What surprise by Easter?" Carmen wondered.

Pedro could only say, "Easter is Sunday after next."

Carmen knew that anyway. The children had been rehearsing for weeks to sing in the Easter service in their plain little chapel which had been a store only a few months ago. They had been bringing their gum-and-candy nickels to buy a white lily for the church on Easter morning. Their teacher had said it would be a very small lily with only one blossom unless the pile of money grew faster. That was why Pedro could count on his fingers and say, "Twelve days till Easter."

Those twelve days were full—school, rehearsing for Easter, saving pennies for the white lily, helping with the housework at home. Once in a while Carmen and Pedro would take a peek at the dead-looking branches in the pickle jar and the milk bottle.

"Look, Pedro!" said Carmen one morning. "Those little lumps on the sides of the sticks! They're growing bigger!"

"They *are* bigger," agreed Pedro.

Each morning Pedro and Carmen looked at the branches. The lumps grew bigger. Then they stood out in little points. Soon they showed a touch of yellow. Then, just three days before Easter, the biggest of them popped open into a yellow blossom. When the children came home from school that afternoon, there were little yellow blossoms scattered all over the branches.

"Remember the butterflies in the flower garden on the farm last summer," said Carmen. "These look like butterflies."

When the children went to choir rehearsal at the church that afternoon, they were full of excitement about the magic branches that had come to life. They found their teacher counting the nickels and looking troubled.

"Easter lilies are so expensive this year," she was saying. "There is money here for only the tiniest one. I had hoped we could have one for each side of the cross on the altar Easter morning."

Carmen's eyes danced, blacker than ever. She had a happy idea.

"Would another kind of flower do?" asked Carmen.

"Depends on the flower." The teacher was thinking of the big bouquets of paper flowers that usually decorated the church. It did seem they should have real flowers on Easter.

"These are magic flowers," said Carmen. "They were just sticks when they came in the mail from the country. We put them in water, just like Priscilla and George wrote, and now there are yellow flowers like butterflies popping out on them."

"Where are these magic flowers?" asked the teacher. She had lived in the country herself and knew how dead branches could come to life in the springtime. "Can I see them—right away?"

"We'll show you," said Pedro. "At our house."

So, with Pedro holding one hand and Carmen holding the other, the teacher walked down the noisy sidewalk to the Nazarios' front door. They climbed the three flights of dark, narrow stairs. The children opened the door and let her into a room that was dim and cheerless, except for two beautiful spots of yellow—the branches in the milk bottle and the branches in the pickle jar. Just as Carmen had said, there were blossoms like yellow butterflies perched up and down the branches that had seemed so dead a week ago.

"Forsythia!" The teacher's voice sang the word. "May we really borrow them for our Easter service?"

"The vases not very nice," apologized Carmen.

"They will fit the vases where we usually have the paper roses," said the teacher. "A big vase of forsythia sprays on either side of the cross, and the tiny Easter lily on the table in front of it! Three days till Easter. These branches will be in full bloom then—a great mass of yellow blossoms."

In the next few days many children climbed the three flights of stairs to gaze at the magic flowers. By Easter morning all the children knew the story of the forsythia. Singing, they marched down the aisle of their plain little chapel: "Christ the Lord is risen today, Alleluia!"

Even the ones who could not understand most of the Easter sermon knew what the minister meant when he said, "These forsythia blossoms tell us the Easter story in two ways. They show us how life goes on and on in what looks dead. And they show us that Jesus lives on in the hearts of children—the ones in the country who sent these branches and the ones of our own neighborhood who shared them."

And at exactly the same time, in a white belfried church far away in the country, Priscilla and George were looking at Easter lilies and thinking about Pedro and Carmen as they sang, "Lives again our glorious King, Alleluia!"

BARTHOLDI'S MOTHER

MOTHER'S DAY OR INDEPENDENCE DAY

"Liberty! Equality! Fraternity!" are three words that the boy Auguste learned from his tall and handsome mother, Charlotte Bartholdi. He learned more than the sound of them or the feel of them on his tongue. He learned what they meant to the people in France in the middle of the last century. Liberty—that everyone in France should be free to think, to speak, and to live his best. Equality—that no man in France was better than another, whether he lived in a tiny hut or a nobleman's palace. Fraternity—that all people of France were brothers.

The boy Auguste loved to listen to his mother's stories of their ancestor General Beysser, a hero of the French Revolution. There was something special in the way she held her head when she told what General Beysser had done to bring freedom to France. As Auguste grew older, he always connected his tall and handsome mother with liberty, equality, and fraternity.

He left the home with its gables, covered balconies, and spire. But he never forgot what his mother had taught him. He grew up to be a sculptor, but he was never satisfied with a statue that was only beautiful. His statues must have a meaning.

Once he was hired to make a statue of a teacher, Édouard de Laboulaye. While Bartholdi was at the De Laboulaye home in the summer of 1865, some guests were invited for dinner. They talked about liberty, equality, and fraternity. The

108

sculptor liked to hear again the ideas and the words that were so dear to his own mother.

Édouard de Laboulaye was a Frenchman who felt that France and America were sister countries that would always work for liberty, equality, and fraternity. At that time the people in America were thinking of freedom for negro slaves, and the people of France were thinking of freedom from neighboring nations, that were threatening to invade their country. That, as De Laboulaye told the friends gathered in his home, made France and America closer sisters than ever.

"Remember how Lafayette helped when America was fighting for its freedom," he said to his friends. "Remember how America's freedom gave France courage to win its own. If a monument should be built in the United States as a memorial to their independence, it should be built by united effort, a common work of both nations."

The word "monument" caught the ears of the young sculptor. A monument representing the liberty that was France and the liberty that was America! What a dream for the son of Charlotte Bartholdi!

While Auguste Bartholdi talked with the people of France about a statue, he wondered how he would represent liberty in bronze or in stone. Édouard de Laboulaye and others liked the idea of the statue and started raising money for its making. It would be the perfect gift from France to celebrate the one hundredth birthday of the United States in 1876. Because the Americans must raise money to build the pedestal, it would become the "common work of both nations."

But how could Auguste Bartholdi tell the story of liberty by a statue? He thought of great men who had worked for liberty—George Washington or Lafayette. But other sculptors had made statues of them. As he went about his other work, there was always the question in the back of his mind—how to create a statue that would make all men think of freedom. He talked it over with his mother, who had taught him to love liberty, equality, and fraternity. Even Charlotte Bartholdi could not suggest a symbol that would stand for the liberty of France and the liberty of America.

Finally the time came for Bartholdi to make his first trip to the United States to talk with Americans about the statue. Still he did not know what symbol to use for liberty. During the voyage across the ocean he was wondering how he could describe the monument to Americans. He had no answers to the questions they would surely ask:

"Where will the statue be located?"

"How will it look?"

"What use will it be?"

The night before the ship was due to dock in New York harbor, he went to bed with not an idea worth giving to the committee he was to meet the next day. A sculptor should have a small model of the statue he plans to make—at least a sketch of it. He had nothing to show.

He woke early the next morning and looked through his porthole. Land was near. He dressed quickly and went on deck. He gazed ahead at something he had never seen before—the skyline of New York City. In those days it was not the skyline of towering buildings we see today. Then, no building was higher than the steeple of Trinity Church. Even so, it was a skyline of beauty—church spires, city buildings, homes spreading out into the country. And all about him ships were going and coming in the busy rivers and bays of New York. He felt the strength and power of a land that was free.

Suddenly his idea came to him. Taking a pencil, he quickly sketched the outline of New York Harbor. Then he pictured from an island in the bay a mighty woman rising with a high-held torch in one hand and something that might have been a big book of laws under her other arm. She was a tall and handsome woman who held her head high, certain that all was well in a world where liberty, equality, and fraternity ruled. Auguste Bartholdi did not have to wonder how the woman of his statue should look. He knew.

Probably you have heard most of the story of the years of

work that stretched between Bartholdi's quick sketch of the statue of Liberty Enlightening the World and the day in 1886 when the statue was dedicated on Bedloe's Island in New York Harbor.

There is one part of this story that is seldom told. On the day when the model of the Statue of Liberty was unveiled in France, Auguste Bartholdi was showered with praise for his work. But he knew who should share credit with him. That evening he invited a friend to go with him to the theater.

"I have a special reason for asking you to come," Bartholdi told his friend.

As Bartholdi and his guest walked into the box, they saw a tall and handsome woman sitting in the corner seat in the front of the box. The guest gasped at sight of her.

"She is the statue," he whispered, "Liberty Enlightening the World!"

"Yes, she is," answered the sculptor. "May I present you to Madame Charlotte Bartholdi—my mother."

Since 1886 the Statue of Liberty has meant the freedom of America to the millions of persons who have sailed in and out of New York Harbor, and to the millions more who have looked at it from shore. Even those who have never been to New York City know by her pictures the tall woman holding up her torch to enlighten the world. But very few know they are looking at the statue of Charlotte Bartholdi, a French mother who taught her son to love liberty, equality, and fraternity. Liberty—that everyone in the world should be free to think, to speak, and to live his best. Equality—that a man is a man whether he lives in a tiny hut or a rich man's palace. Fraternity—that all men everywhere are brothers.

THIRTY-TWO LANGUAGES

UNITED NATIONS DAY

Of course Bob Wright had always heard about the United Nations ever since he could remember. He had studied about it in school back in the U.S.A. Always in October, at Scout meeting, at school, and at church, he had helped celebrate United Nations Day. One year he brought a dime to help buy a United Nations flag for school. Once he had a few lines in a United Nations play for Scouts. One year the junior choir learned a "Song of Peace" to sing in church, but he thought less about the words than about the itchy collar of his junior-choir robe. Of course they said a pledge of allegiance to the United Nations at least once a year at school. Bob had not needed to learn it, because it was always written on the blackboard. He never thought much about the words. When he thought about the United Nations at all, he pictured a lot of little countries that had agreed to "play ball" with his own great country.

All that was when Bob was back home in the United States. Then Bob's family moved to the Middle East, where his father worked with the World Health Organization, the branch of the United Nations that is trying to improve health conditions all over the world. While he sat in the big four-motored plane, zooming along at better than three hundred miles an hour, Bob began to learn what a huge world the United Nations represented.

But it was when he started to school in his new home, in the capital city of a Middle Eastern country, that he really began to think of different nations working together. It was a school for boys and girls whose fathers had come from other lands. Some were working for some branch of the United Nations, such as the Technical Assistance Program or the Food and Agriculture Organization. Some represented their various countries in the embassies and consulates of Pakistan, Switzerland, Denmark, China, Poland. Some were missionaries. Some were technicians from America working with the Foreign Operations Administration, part of the United States' attempt to help other countries.

Luckily for Bob the language of the school was English. The boys and girls from lands with other languages had to do their best with English. With schoolmates able to speak thirty-two different languages, Bob began to get the feel of the idea of the United Nations. He noticed that the best artist in the school was a quiet Armenian boy. The girl who could make them almost hold their breaths as they watched her dance came from Russia. Boys from Holland, Germany, and Turkey were the best players on the volleyball team. Nobody passed his Scouting tests faster than Pavlos from Greece. And Bob's mother kept saying that she had never seen anyone prettier than the girls from India, especially on the days when they wore their bright-colored saris. Bob found to his surprise that being an American did not make him important. With every day that passed, he admired his new friends more and his own self less. In fact, as he saw how good the rest of them were, he was beginning to feel almost too small and unimportant.

Then something happened that made him feel exactly his right size and made him feel that he could take his own part in the little United Nations in which he was living. The school was preparing a Parents' Day Program on the theme "One World." It was to open with a salute to the United Nations flag and a pledge of allegiance spoken in thirty-two different languages. Choosing the ones to speak in some of the languages was easy, because the children speaking those languages were few; but the honor of representing the United

States of America might come to any one of a hundred boys and girls.

Every boy and girl in the upper grades knew the teachers were talking it over. When the pupils overheard something like, ". . . has a good voice to be heard outdoors," those with strong voices hoped they were being mentioned. And when they overheard something like, ". . . acts as though living by the pledge," they began to feel sorry about the times they had said mean things about the countries of their schoolmates. Bob kept hoping that the teachers would forget how he acted during his first days of school when he thought that he was important because he was an American.

Finally the announcement came from the principal. "The American to say our United Nations pledge of allegiance will be the boy we feel has learned the most in the shortest time about appreciating people of other nations than his own—Bob Wright."

Now Bob knew that he must really learn that pledge of allegiance to the United Nations. He must learn its words and its meaning. He must no longer think of the United Nations as a group of small countries gathered around his own big country. He knew now that the United Nations was made up of many great countries whose people were like his new school friends. He knew now that only by working with people of these other nations could we have a world that would be always at peace.

That was what Bob tried to put into his voice on the day of the "One World" program. Together the thirty-two of them marched out onto the athletic field and faced their parents in the rows of seats. Together they saluted the United Nations flag of blue and white. Then one by one they gave their pledge of allegiance, each in the language of his own country: "I pledge allegiance to my country and to the United Nations of which it is a part, one world brotherhood of peaceful nations with liberty and justice for all."

Through the program of songs and folk dances of different

lands Bob's one-world feeling grew within him. Even if he had been wearing a junior-choir robe with an itchy collar, he would have felt the real meaning of the "Song of Peace," as the whole school and audience together sang it at the close of the program. They sang in English, but they were thinking and feeling in the tongues of thirty-two lands:

> This is my song, O God of all the nations,
> A song of peace for lands afar and mine;
> This is my home, the country where my heart is,
> Here are my hopes, my dreams, my holy shrine,
> But other hearts in other lands are beating,
> With hopes and dreams as true and high as mine.
>
> My country's skies are bluer than the ocean,
> And sunlight beams on clover leaf and pine;
> But other lands have sunlight too, and clover,
> And skies are ev'rywhere as blue as mine.
> Oh, hear my song, thou God of all the nations,
> A song of peace for their land and for mine.

The "One World" program described was given at the Community School at Tehran, Iran, May, 1953. The "Song of Peace" is sung to the tune *Finlandia*. The words, by Lloyd Stone, are copyright 1934 by Lorenz Publishing Co. and are used by permission.

NOEL, THE CHRISTMAS BABY

CHRISTMAS

It was a moonlit Christmas Eve in Jerusalem in the year 1925. The families of the American Colony had thought of a lovely way to celebrate—so lovely a way that they wondered why they had never thought of it before. They were going outside the Jerusalem Wall through the Jaffa Gate to follow the road toward Bethlehem as far as the place known as the Shepherds' Field. There they would sing Christmas carols in full view of the twinkling lights of distant Bethlehem.

While they sang "O Little Town of Bethlehem" or "Silent Night" or "The First Noel," they would look up at the stars and they would look across at Bethlehem lying still in the moonlight. It would be easy in such a setting to think back to that night so long ago when Jesus was born in a Bethlehem stable. The shepherds, the wise men, Mary, Joseph, and the Baby would seem near and very real.

Mrs. Vester had promised to lead the singing while her family of six children joined the neighbors in the carols. She had been delayed by a Christmas party in a school for girls, and so she was hurrying toward her home by the Damascus Gate. The songs of Christmas were in her heart as she hummed the carols that they would soon be singing in the Shepherd's Field toward Bethlehem. Mrs. Vester was in a hurry, but her long habit of helping people was so strong that she had to stop when she met a sick Arab woman carrying a bundle of dirty rags. The way the woman leaned on her husband showed that she was very weak.

Mrs. Vester knew their language, Arabic, so she asked, "Where are you going?"

"Only Allah knows," answered the man.

The bundle of rags stirred in the arms of the Arab woman. It was a tiny baby, not more than three days old. Then the story came out. The young mother was very sick. From her village she had ridden six hours on donkeyback, her baby in her arms, to come to the out-patient department of the city hospital. But it was a holiday, and the clinic was closed. Where could she go?

Mrs. Vester thought of her family and friends waiting to go to the Shepherds' Field to sing Christmas carols and rest their eyes on the lights of distant Bethlehem twinkling in the moonlight. She remembered how she had been looking forward to this carol-sing in worship of the Baby, who was born in a stable because there was no room for him in the inn. Then Mrs. Vester looked at the sick mother, tiny baby, and discouraged father who had no place to spend the night. And because Mrs. Vester had the Christian habit of helping people, she knew there was a better way to worship the Baby born in a stable than to sing about him.

So she found a place for the father to spend the night. She telephoned her husband and told him to take the children to the carol-sing in the Shepherds' Field without waiting for her. She managed to have a stretcher brought to carry the sick mother and the baby to the hospital. Then, because many of the nurses were off duty for the holidays, Mrs. Vester took care of both mother and baby until they were clean and fed and comfortable for the night. By that time it was too late for her to worship the Baby born in a manger by singing Christmas carols under the stars on the Shepherds' Field. Her heart was glad, however, because she had worshiped him a better way.

The next morning was full of Christmas fun for the Vester children in the stone house by the Damascus Gate. The mother had forgotten her disappointment in missing the carol-sing. She had even forgotten about the sick woman and her baby until she happened to look out her window. There stood the father from the village, the tiny baby in his arms. Mrs. Vester hurried out to talk to him.

"Will you take care of my baby?" asked the sad-faced father. "My wife died last night. My baby cannot possibly live if I take him back to my home in a cave."

Because Mrs. Vester had the Christian habit of helping, she did not stop to figure out whether she had time or space or money to care for another baby. She simply held out her arms for the tiny baby—and named him "Noel."

And that was the beginning of the baby hospital and clinic of the American Colony in Jerusalem. Noel needed a room and nurse, and there were other babies who needed help. Soon there were so many babies that Noel's room was not big enough to hold them. A stone hospital was built which connected with the Vesters' stone house by the Damascus Gate. Then the Vesters turned their own stone house into a hospital and moved to a new home outside the walls of Jerusalem. Later another wing was added to the house to serve as a clinic where mothers—sometimes as many as a hundred a day—bring their babies for care and treatment. An architect made plans for adding rooms on the roof for a surgical ward. Now there are many clean white cribs in the baby hospital, each one with its thin, dark-eyed, Arab baby being nursed back to health. Some stay only a few days, but some stay many months. And when each baby goes home, its mother has learned from the nurses how to keep him well. Health is being brought to the babies and small children in the crowded twisting streets of Old Jerusalem.

And all of this happened because Mrs. Vester knew that the best way to worship the baby Jesus was to help the people he loved. She knew that singing Christmas carols was good, but that living them was better.

This incident was told to me by Mrs. Vester in Jerusalem. It is told on pp. 304-6 of *Our Jerusalem* by Bertha Spafford Vester (Doubleday, 1950). Used by permission.

THE MITTEN TREE

CHRISTMAS

The two balsam trees were brothers. Starting from seeds from a cone of the same big balsam tree, they grew side by side. For ten years the snows of winter had weighted down their branches and the sun of summer had made dappled brightness on their fragrant green needles. For ten years squirrels jumped from one tree to the other, while chickadees and juncos twittered in the branches. The balsam brothers expected to live together forever in the forest that was their home.

But one day in early winter there were heavy footsteps in the forest, not the light clip of a deer's hoofs or the rustle of a chipmunk's scuttling feet. Men with saws walked among the trees and cut the young trees that were most straight and perfect. The two balsam brothers were among the first to be chosen.

They were dragged over the snow and loaded into a truck to go bouncing and rumbling to a faraway city. Still side by side, the balsams found themselves leaning against a store behind a sign, "CHRISTMAS TREES FOR SALE." There were evergreen trees all about them, trees without roots. They watched people come and take the trees away in cars, one tree at a time. At any minute one of them might be taken, and they would be lost to each other.

"I need two trees," they heard someone say, "two trees as nearly alike as possible."

"These two are as like as two brothers," they heard the tree salesman say, "and beauties too."

"I'll buy them," answered the voice.

119

The two balsams were loaded into the trunk of a car. They went bouncing through the city street and nodding their green tips to everyone they passed. The car stopped in front of a big building with a tall steeple. The trees were carried into a large room where there were many chairs the right sizes for small children, big children, and middle-sized children.

One tree was set on one side of a platform and the other tree was set on the other. It seemed that they were still going to be alike. But no! One tree stood alone and forgotten. The other tree was the center of a crowd of boys and girls who began loading its branches with all sorts of gay and pretty things— colored glass balls, long strings of shining tinsel, angels with wings like gold, festoons of red and green lights, dozens of striped candy canes.

"My turn will come next," thought the empty tree.

But no! When the one tree was completely covered with shining beauty, the boys and girls cleared up the litter of paper and boxes. Then they took a last admiring look at the trimmed tree and left the room with never a glance at the bare tree.

The two trees stood side by side in the darkness. A moonbeam touched the empty tree, but there was nothing to sparkle back. Another moonbeam slid through the window and made sparkles on the tinsel of the other. For the first time the brothers were not alike. For the first time there was a feeling between them that was not quite brotherly.

The next day the doors of the big room opened again. In came boys and girls, each one with a package in his hands. The sparkling tree preened its branches till its glass bells tinkled. The empty tree stood still as could be and hoped nobody would notice its plainness.

Then an amazing thing happened. With scarcely a look at the trimmed tree, the boys and girls walked toward the empty tree. As each child approached it, he unwrapped the package he carried in his hands. Out of each package came something bright and gay—a pair of colorful warm mittens fastened together by a pretty ribbon or cord. Each child hung his pair of mittens on the plain balsam tree. The tall children covered the high branches, and the little children covered the low ones. Soon the mitten tree had far more colors than the tree trimmed with glass and tinsel. There were red mittens, yellow mittens, blue mittens, green mittens. There were mittens knitted with stripes and with checks. There were mittens with animal pictures knitted into them.

When the tree was mitten-covered from its tip to its lowest branch, the children formed a circle around it and sang the song of the "Mitten Tree." Then someone brought a big carton labeled:

> Mitten Tree Project
> American Friends Service Committee
> 20 South 12th Street
> Philadelphia 7, Pennsylvania

Into this box went all the mittens. The tree was bare again. But it did not care. It heard someone saying, "These mittens are for children whose fingers are cold. Wherever they live, we are sending these warm mittens so that their fingers may be warm."

The mitten tree, empty once more, looked across at his sparkling brother and was glad that he was the one chosen to bring warmth and comfort to those children of the cold fingers. He was glad that he could help instead of just being pretty and sparkling.

This story may be adapted to fit other Christmas-giving projects.

CIRO'S BIGGER WORLD

CHRISTMAS

Ciro's world was very small. It consisted of bomb-wrecked houses and rubble-built huts where families who could not pay rent had lived since the war. It was bounded on one side by the beautiful Bay of Naples and on the other side by new apartment houses for families whose fathers had regular work.

Cars, going he knew not where, whizzed past Ciro's scarred door. Ships entered the harbor from somewhere, then puffed away till their wisp of black smoke disappeared where blue sky and blue sea seemed to meet. Ciro often looked up to watch a plane speeding away beyond where eye could see. He never wondered about the unknown travelers or the places they were going. That is, he never wondered till the day he walked to meet music.

Like every child of Naples, Ciro had music within him that no amount of dirt or hunger or crowding could quiet. So when he heard children singing a new song "Notte Benigna," he walked to find them. He stood with them looking up at a brightly trimmed fir tree on the small balcony of a building that was once a warehouse. If he had had clothes good enough for school, Ciro would have known that the words spelled in lights under the tree were *Casa Mia*, Italian for "my home." It was the children who told him what the words meant.

"We have games and school and clinic," said Anna.

"And something to eat every day," said Vittorio.

"And packages from America," said Dinacci.

"And friends," said Carmellina.

Humming the new tune, Ciro followed them inside the

settlement house. A smiling woman named Miss Rosa welcomed him, "You may watch the boys and girls your age rehearse their Christmas play."

She gave him a place to sit in the back corner of a big room full of black-smocked boys and girls.

Sitting there the next few mornings, Ciro discovered what each child represented in their play "The International Christmas Tree." Pasquale, one of the bigger boys, was Santa Claus, "Papa Natale" to the Italian children. Luisa, Guiseppe, Maria, Salvatore, Nicola, and their friends were playing that each was a child from a different place, from countries called Spain, Holland, Japan, Sweden, Africa, and other names. Vittorio alone was acting the Italian boy he really was. He turned a big ball of blue and other colors, a "globe of the world" they called it.

At first, Turkey, Switzerland, England, and China were only words to Ciro. Watching the rehearsals and listening to Miss Rosa, he learned that these words stood for places where children lived and worked and played games and watched for Papa Natale. Ciro learned that in all these countries boys and girls were singing "Notte Benigna," though they pronounced it differently: "Stille Nacht" in Germany, "Noche de Paz" in Spain, "Silent Night" in England and America. Ciro learned that the globe in Vittorio's hands showed where these places were in relation to one another. But these faraway lands seemed only a dream to a boy who lived in a rubble-built hut and sat in the back corner of the room at Casa Mia to watch and to listen.

"We must find a part for Ciro," Miss Rosa would say. But the teachers were all so busy with their Christmas preparations which included making round-the-world costumes from the least useful clothes that came in the big burlap bales from America. There was no time to think up a new part for Ciro.

"At least you can be an usher," Miss Rosa promised. But she had not reckoned with the United States Navy!

On the day before the program fifty children of Casa Mia

rode to the shore in navy trucks and then boarded the U.S.S. "Chloris" for a Christmas party. There are no better hosts in all the world than one hundred sailors who are a bit homesick for their own children, their smaller brothers and sisters, or nephews and nieces. A doll for every girl! A big ball for every boy! Soap, candy, and a can of orange juice for every child! Games! Songs! And such food!

Most of the children carried their extra food home. Dinacci asked permission to take his turkey bone home to his brother. Anna and Pasquale carried their paper cups of candy and nuts home to their grandparents. Carmellina, who had never had much experience with ice cream, tucked her full paper cup in the corner of her doll box to carry home to her sister.

But Vittorio just ate and ate and ate. Whenever the sailors offered him more food, he smiled and said, "Si," which is Italian for "Yes." He said, "Si," to more turkey, more ice cream, more candy.

The next day when Ciro sat in his corner watching the children put on their costumes for the play, everyone was there but Vittorio. Luisa became a Spanish girl in a bright full skirt. Guiseppe became a Swiss boy wearing a felt hat with a feather in it. Salvatore became a Japanese boy in a bright kimono. Pasquale became Papa Natale with stuffed-out stomach inside some red pajamas.

The clock ticked nearer to the time for the entertainment. Guests were arriving in the big room next to them. But still the globe of the world waited for Vittorio.

"He has a stomach-ache," explained Maria, peeking out from her Eskimo hood. She knew because her family shared a room with Vittorio's family. "He ate too much at the sailors' party yesterday."

Then the teachers and the children all waved their hands and talked at once. It was Miss Rosa who first noticed Ciro. He had taken a step forward from his corner, then stopped, wondering how bold he dared be.

"Do you know Vittorio's lines, Ciro?" Miss Rosa asked.

"I know them," answered Ciro's shy, eager voice.

"Do you know what he does in the play?" she asked.

"I know." Ciro was close beside the teachers, his hands clasped behind his back to keep them from reaching out for the globe.

They heard more footsteps and many voices in the big room. Mothers, fathers, grandparents, sisters, brothers, and neighbors had arrived for the program.

"I know you can do it." Miss Rosa put the globe in Ciro's hands. She hurried him into the pajamas which Vittorio was supposed to be wearing. "Now you look ready for bed on Christmas Eve."

The next room was suddenly quiet. Then there was music. The white-smocked kindergarten children were singing "Away in a Manger," as only children of Naples can sing.

The song ended. Globe in hand, Ciro entered the room full of guests. He walked across the stage, yawned as he had seen Vittorio yawn, and sat down on the bed which had been placed near a gift-filled Christmas tree. Then he began to wonder aloud, as he had heard Vittorio.

"Papa Natale will be coming soon." Ciro slowly turned the globe. "I wonder how the rest of the world celebrates Christmas?"

The lights twinkled. Ciro studied the globe. There was the tap-tap of wooden shoes. Anna, in white cap and apron, walked toward him.

"Shall I tell you about Christmas in Holland?" she asked.

"Please" Ciro held the globe toward Anna, who pointed at the small pink spot that was Holland.

"We call Papa Natale, 'Saint Nicholas,'" she said. He comes riding on Saint Nicholas' Eve. We leave our wooden shoes filled with hay to feed his big white horse. In the morning we find gifts in place of the hay."

One by one the costumed children entered. Luisa told how the three kings rode their camels through Spain and left gifts. Guiseppe explained how carefully Swiss men carved wooden crèche figures to tell the story of Jesus' birth. Andrea remembered how sweet the homes of Sweden smelled with freshly cut Christmas pines on either side of the door and juniper branches spread on the floor. Fabio described Germany's Christmas trees and sugar-decorated, toy-shaped ginger cakes. Guido told how choir boys sang Christmas carols in the English churches. Lorenzo described Christmas pageants and "white gifts" of unknown children in American churches. The globe in Ciro's hand suddenly stood for something big and alive.

Then Papa Natale dashed on the stage. It was hard to believe that he was only Pasquale as he began taking little bags of candy from the tree for the children. Ciro waited for Papa Natale's last words, the part of the play he liked best: "You children are all equal in all parts of the world. You speak different languages. You live in homes built in different ways. You have different customs. But you can all live together happily. All of you are God's children."

"Notte Benigna," sung by the first graders, made happy music in Ciro's mind as he walked from Casa Mia toward his wretched piece of a house. He knew that children all over his newly discovered world were glad because a very special Baby had been born on that *notte benigna* so long ago.

A car whizzed by. Ciro, walking in its dust, wondered if it was going to Switzerland or France, where there were children so much like him. A motor pounded overhead. Ciro looked up. Perhaps the plane was carrying fathers to be with their children at Christmas time in Greece or Japan. A ship was steaming out of the beautiful Bay of Naples. Ciro watched till there was only a wisp of black smoke where blue sky seemed to meet blue sea. Was the ship going to Africa or Spain or America? Wherever it went, there would be children who played games, watched for Papa Natale, and sang "Notte Benigna" in their own language.

Ciro's world had grown very large. He knew, surely, that it was full of God's children who were ever so much like him.

Based on a letter from Hulda Stettler, social worker for the Congregational Christian Service Committee in Naples, Italy.